D1648359

Chrysalis 9

Chrysalis 9

EDITED BY ROY TORGESON

DOUBLEDAY & COMPANY, INC.

GARDEN CITY, NEW YORK

1981

All of the characters in this book
are fictitious, and any resemblance
to actual persons, living or dead,
is purely coincidental.

First Edition

ISBN: 0-385-17251-6
Library of Congress Catalog Card Number 81-640147
Copyright © 1981 by Roy Torgeson
All Rights Reserved
Printed in the United States of America

For Seven Days in June
when Dee and I transformed
Reality into Fantasy while
displaying remarkable creativity
not only solving but transcending
all problems of density, surface
tension, and gravity.

Contents

Introduction

Here's *Chrysalis 9*, another richly varied selection of the very best science fiction and fantasy stories being written. Karl Hansen is making his sixth appearance in one of my anthologies, and Glenn Chang, Tanith Lee, Pat Murphy, Margaret St. Clair, Al Sarrantonio, Somtow Sucharitkul, and Steve Rasnic Tem are also making repeat performances. On the other hand, "new blood" is supplied by Patrick H. Adkins, Cynthia Felice, and Nicholas V. Yermakov. It's a real pleasure to have this mix of both old and new friends, and I guarantee that they will provide you with hours of reading enjoyment.

The lead story, *A Child of Earth and Starry Heaven,* is a gripping contemporary fantasy by 1980 John W. Campbell Award nominee Somtow Sucharitkul. When I wrote to Somtow asking for a bit of information about the story, he jokingly replied, "*A Child of Earth and Starry Heaven* is a story that started off— What if Ingmar Bergman had directed *The Bad News Bears* . . . and it was set on the Orient Express?" It really isn't about this at all, but after reading the story you'll understand why I couldn't resist including Somtow's bit of whimsy.

A Child of Earth and Starry Heaven is about a young boy, who is a great baseball enthusiast, traveling through Europe by train with his mother, sister, and dying father. Death constantly lurks in the wings and is eventually brought onstage and confronted when the young boy learns of his very special relationship to Him. What follows is a highly original and absorbing exploration of our concept of death in general and the personal death which is locked up inside of us all.

Nicholas V. Yermakov writes tough, hard-hitting, and often brutal stories, and damn good ones at that. *Tomorrow Mourning* is a *good* story, but more low-key than anything by Nick that I have read before. The "tomorrow morning" in this story takes place twenty-five years after a man has been placed in suspended animation awaiting a cure for leukemia. Upon awakening he asks to see his former lover, who has aged, matured, and changed over twenty-five years, while he himself has remained both physically and emotionally the same. *Tomorrow Mourning* is a very different kind of love story that will leave you with a lot to think about.

The Hashed Brown Buggy, by Margaret St. Clair, is a bizarre little tale that almost defies description. Dealing with death and decay, it is about living and exploring the expanded present and the wider now, while the main character, Elel, is both monstrously alien and sympathetically familiar. See what I mean? *The Hashed Brown Buggy* is a story that you'll simply have to experience for yourself.

Glenn Chang's *Dancing in the Dark* is a refreshingly original treatment of the "first contact" theme. The alien entity is a bunch of particles moving through space, a literal cosmic will-o'-the-wisp known as the Anomaly, or Charybdis to its friends. Its first contact is not with human beings, but with LOBO, earth's most sophisticated orbiting computer. Since LOBO was created and programmed by a human being and his only contact has been with humans, this first contact with an utterly alien entity produces some very strange reactions. He lapses into catatonic states, he babbles charming but seemingly inane chatter and gives every impression of being psychotic. Wolf Kohara, LOBO's creator, with help from *his* psychotherapist, then struggles to break through to LOBO. After all, she had helped Wolf through a very tough time and maybe she could do the same with LOBO. *Dancing in the Dark* is fascinating, and Glenn's playful use of words (LOBO's inane babbling) is a pure joy to read.

Orange Blossom Time, by Pat Murphy, is a strange and compelling love story. Set in a dying city, it tells of a most unusual woman who can travel through time but only as long as she does nothing to affect the "natural" flow of events. She can do nothing to prevent the destruction of society and she is powerless to prevent the death of her lover. She can, however, bring him a brief moment of happiness before the end. This may not change the world, but it is still very important.

Steve Rasnic Tem is the most talented new writer of short horror fiction to come along since Ramsey Campbell. High praise, but I think that it is well deserved. Steve has two stories in *Chrysalis 9: Again, the Hit-and-Run* is a mere 750 words long and *The Sound of Hawkwings Dissolving* is five times this length. But both are *perfect*. Not a single word is wasted and every word used is the right one. Rarely have I seen so much emotion packed into so small a space.

A Good Place to Be, by Cynthia Felice, opens with Linda and Joe lying in bed together. Linda is thinking that being in bed with Joe is a good place to be, when suddenly she realizes that they are not alone. Her friend and confidante, Sally, is also there, just as surely as if she had walked through the door and stood watching them. But Sally isn't standing at the door. She is a mile away and in Linda's head at the same time. Sally is Linda's crippled and bedridden roommate with whom she shares a telepathic relationship. It has been a good one for both of them, but now it seems that Sally also thinks that being in bed with Joe is a good place to be. A good place for *Sally* to be, that is.

Karl Hansen's *The Ballad of Lady Blue* is set in a far future in which genetic engineering has become commonplace. It is the third story in this series to appear in *Chrysalis*, but chronologically it takes place first and tells of the third generation born after the genetic revolution.

After the recombinant revolution each individual's genome was carefully constructed to represent the optimal pattern of DNA molecules. The short life-span, necessary for the forces of natural selection to operate, was no longer needed. Indeed, the genes responsible for predetermined senescence had been repressed, so previous "natural" aging no longer occurred. Freed from degenerative disease, there was no finite limit to the human life-span. Practical immortality had been attained. Provided one could avoid natural hazards and trauma, one could live in perpetual youth. Or at least the first and second generations could. Luellan belonged to the third and *there was something terribly wrong with his generation.*

That They Be Saved, by Al Sarrantonio, is a grim story. In terms of mood, it starts off at the bottom and goes steadily downhill thereafter. It's the kind of story I like to read when I feel angry, frustrated, and depressed. Things may be bad, but not *this* bad. Not yet, anyway.

Hunting the Dragonblood, by Patrick H. Adkins, is written around an ironic twist on the "Johnny Appleseed" myth and warns against our waste of natural resources. Beyond this, however, it is a warm and tender story about an old man and his young grandson, one that captures a mood or feeling reminiscent of the post-Holocaust stories written by the late, great Edgar Pangborn. *Hunting the Dragonblood* is one of those rare stories that make you feel glad to be a part of the human race.

No doubt about it, *Gemini* by Tanith Lee is one of the strangest *and* most terrifying stories I have ever read. Set in an eerie future world, it tells of a hauntingly strange woman named Geminna and an ever-present "something" that she simply calls "*It.*" Always within Geminna, always a part of her, *It* watches, *It* listens, and when need be *It* acts! Subtly written and frighteningly understated, *Gemini* is a masterpiece of quiet, almost gentle horror.

As always I thank the authors for allowing me to share in their fantastic creativity.

ROY TORGESON
New York City
April 1981

A Child of Earth and Starry Heaven

BY
SOMTOW SUCHARITKUL

we know that death is evil
if death were good
the gods themselves would die
                    —Sappho

what? death has a sense of humor?
                    —Euripides, *Alcestis*

When I think back to the year when I was twelve and we all skipped school and rode the rails all over Europe with the parents muttering on about value-readjustments and expanding our experiential cosmos—

I see Dad, farting to death on the Athens–Paris Express. And the crammed air getting stinkier and stinkier, and the fields of Yugoslavia unreeling like a sickly-green clothroll, and I hear Mom's knit-knit-knitting. And Sophie too, knit-knit-knitting like a wee color Xerox, them with their black hair bunned up and their dresses faded green floral prints and Sophie with those pink shreds of leftover yarn juryrigging her pigtails . . .

I'm a hell of a lot older now, and I've read books that tell you how the light falls on the ruins at Sounion and stuff like that. Yah. Jesus. I saw it. It wasn't like that at all. It was—think of the sky as a bright blue safe dropping from a cosmic skyscraper. That's the thing I remember. The ruins . . . take 'em or leave 'em. But the sky and then the mists at Delphi in the dawn. Creepy. Oh, Greece, Greece, Greece. I'm going to go back.

After Greece the world got sick. I mean, Dad got sicker and sicker and I knew that dying wasn't anything like in *Love Story*. It's as glamorous as a garbage can in the Bronx.

It's nervousness. It's wondering how tactless you can get. It's sitting in nonsmoking compartments in cramped European trains and not daring to get up and leave because he'll think you don't love him. It's the fart that makes you cry.

And it was so inconvenient. Because that year I was supposed to be at home and practicing to be a hitter for the whatever team I wanted to be a hitter for at the time even though I couldn't hit worth shit. And my world was falling in ruins all around me as we traipsed like demons from hotel to *demi-pension* to inn to YMCA to sleeping cars.

It was so hard to believe he *was* dying. Dad looked like a seedy stevedore from Naples—which is just what *his* dad was—but in real life he was Professor Emilio Caro and taught comparative lit at some college round the corner and had a string of Ph.D.s that stretched all the way from Cambridge Massachusetts to Cambridge England. Yah. In the compartment he'd have the whole of the seat that was facing the way the train was going all to himself so he could stretch out. And he'd erupt now and then like a noisy volcano spewing brimstone. When he was better he'd sit back and pontificate. It was like that all the way through Yugoslavia.

Mom was Greek and just beautiful. I look a lot like her, but I'm just wiry and muscly enough to look cute and not faggy. If she didn't wear those shabby clothes, and if she didn't sit there just knitting, her eyes downcast, not even noticing her four-year-old daughter's awkward mimicking . . . I always changed my clothes every few hours. I was compulsive about it. And frankly, I was scared because of all the fart gas, thinking it might have germs. It's so hard to be afraid of being near your own father.

The train wasn't like Amtrak. No way. There were these corridors down the side and individualized compartments with seats like the sofas you donate to the Salvation Army.

When I could—like pretending to go to the bathroom—I'd stalk the corridors. I'd lean out of the windows until I almost fell out or until the guard caught me or until the krauts from the next compartment came out to jabber and smoke. They always treated me like I wasn't there. Well, I was a kid. I was used to shoving off.

A couple hours from the Austrian border and we'd just trundled past one of those Hollywood villages, a little grimier than the brochure, and I was leaning out again and thinking about Greece and baseball and death—

Like, you know, Greece and death. There was this play we saw at Epidauros, there was this drama festival there . . . it was called *Alcestis* and it was by Euripides. There was this guy Admetos, see, who'd gotten Death to agree to let him off if he could find someone else to buy it in his place. So he got his own wife. Then his friend Heracles (that's Hercules to you philistines) came visiting just in time for the funeral, and he got so mad that he went down to the underworld and wrestled Death to the ground (just like those FBI agents. Yah.) So they all got off scotfree. That was a weird idea and it gave me a nightmare at the hotel. With Dad dying and all. They wore these masks and their voices came echohowling round and round the enormous arena and the mask for Death was worse than something out of *The Exorcist.* . . .

And baseball? Well. There was this kid called Chet Perkins the Pumpkin who pitched for the Annandale Coca-Cola Tomcats or something. He was (as Dad said in a more lucid moment) "querulous, belligerent, beady-eyed and hirsute." (I wrote it down. Dad's pontifications were pretty damn funny sometimes, when you forgot he was on the verge of croaking.) When he got on the field he turned into a blubbery Baryshnikov, though, and so when he beaned me I knew it was no accident. Next season I was going to bust the Pumpkin into a gooey pulp. So what if they sent me off the field.

Well—I had my head in the wind and my hair was all tangled and dusty and billowing and I was pressed hard against the train and the chugchugging and it felt, you know, sexy . . .

I felt a stab in the ribs and nearly fell out.

"Don't do that, dummy!" I gasped.

"Mommy wants you back, Jody."

"Sophie—"

"Yeah, I know. I'm a pain in the ath," she chirped sweetly. I slid the door panel open and watched the point of light whisk across the peeling varnish . . .

"I'm here, Mom." They'd been fighting.

I could tell by the tongue-bitten pent-up smile that froze on Mom's face. I could tell by Dad's staring fixedly out of the window as if the telegraph poles were lines of Dante or pictures of naked women. And the smell hit me hard.

"Yah, can I get Dad something?" I said.

"No. I just thought it'd be nice if we were all together, Jody," Mom said, and went on with her knitting.

In a few minutes Dad had fallen asleep, and the snorting and the farting began to syncopate with the chugging of the train like progressive jazz. Sophie suddenly conked out too. This travelling was a bit much for a kid like that sometimes. And the sun was setting ahead of us somewheres, making the meadows all eerie and bloody.

So it was just me and Mom awake then and I knew something was going to happen. I knew she was going to tell me something. We had a special thing going, me and Mom. Going to Greece had confirmed it somehow. Because . . . I had *recognized* everything there. I mean like the incredible blueness of the sky. I mean I knew it was the way things are meant to be, and that the smog over Brooklyn and even the sun shining through the palms in Florida . . . were just imitations. We'd lived in so many places and none of them had ever been home. And this was. Sophie and Dad—well, they were the wop contingent. I'm allowed to say that because *I'm* one, and I don't mean . . . oh shit.

"What were you fighting about?"

Mom said, "Do you remember *Alcestis?*"

"The play in Epidauros?"

"Uh huh." Knit-knit. And the sunset in her eyes. "What would you say if I took Dad's place?"

I started. "He'd never let you!" I said. She shushed me quickly and pointed to Dad, who was snoring and smiling in his sleep. "Well he wouldn't, would he?" I whispered. "Anyway you're just torturing yourself over it. Life isn't a play by Euripides, Mom."

"I guess."

"The man in the play was an asshole."

"I guess." Knit.

We didn't talk for an hour after that. I was really disturbed because she'd talked almost like it were possible to switch around and die instead of someone else. I tried to forget about it and sat there in the smelly dark, imagining myself batting the Pumpkin's pitches into his face and the blood spurting. Jesus. Yah.

So we got to the Austrian border and the train stopped for us to get our papers stamped, and then I had to help Dad go to the bathroom.

Well—this old man and this kid come charging out from a cubicle in the station and you know what they're thinking, those slimy

Passkontrollebeamterscheissekopf characters with their glittertacky uniforms and pug faces.

Yah, dying isn't glamorous at all. I thought that all the way back to the compartment. It's dirty and disgusting and gross.

Later—we were stalled at the station for a couple hours—me and Dad were talking on a bench together. He was wrapped in a gray fur coat even though it was the middle of night. He had his arm around me and I was uneasy. I remember the bench: one of the planks was missing from the seat and it had a green lacquery look in the harsh station lights . . .

"Dad," I said, "Mom just made a really weird suggestion." (I remembered the Greek chorus moving like dancing dolls across the proscenium . . . and Death's face. In the nightmare the face would jump up at me and stare me down. There were times when I saw the mask of Death almost emerging from behind Dad's face . . .)

"Your momma very weird, ragazzo," Dad said in his best spaghetti-sauce-commercial accent that always made me laugh, only I didn't; and then I was afraid his feelings would be hurt so I forced out a chuckle that choked me.

"But what exactly did she mean?" I said, persisting.

"Your mother's a witch you know. Your grandad always tried to ward off the evil eye when she came to their house. At first. I thought she was going to stop all that—"

He looked at me and then stopped talking, as though he'd said too much. "What am I saying, ragazzo?" he said. "I shouldn't be sitting here badmouthing my own wife now, should I? Well I take it back. She's no witch . . . even though she thinks she is . . . but she's headstrong, strong-willed, willful, foolhardly."

"That was a clever thing to say, Dad," I said, filing it away.

"Verbal concatenations *are* cool, aren't they?" he said, taking a slug from one of those funny teeny continental coke bottles. "Especially beginning each word with the previous final syllable . . ."

I hugged him. It was hard. It seemed like under the big coat there was nothing at all, an emptiness. It felt almost as though he were dissolving under the pressure of my arms. He handed me the bottle and I had to have some, even though it made me queasy.

A breeze whooshed over and lifted the stench a little. "So what did *you* think about Momma's proposal?" he said.

"Dad, you'd never let her anyway! I know you, Daddy! Admetos was an asshole."

Was it the glare from the overhead sodium arcs? He wouldn't meet my eyes and I didn't want him to try.

The train rumbled into the dark night. It was our second night on the Express; Sophie and I shared one cabin of the sleeping car and Mom and Dad had one about four cabins down. We sat in second class in the daytime, understand . . . but with Dad sick we couldn't compromise about the sleeper.

Well, I couldn't sleep. The moon shone into the cabin which wasn't more than a cubbyhole, and I couldn't close the blinds because it was kind of a night light for Sophie. So I got down from the top bunk and changed my clothes a couple of times and washed my face and hands in the midget basin that only ran cold water, like I wanted to scrub every last germ into oblivion. I'd look into the mirror over the basin and comb my hair over and over. Finally I got out my baseball bat from the satchel and swung a couple of times, and then stuffed it back into the bag. *You'll never be any good,* I told me, *in spite of the fancy aluminum bat and the spiffy satchel and the classy fifty dollar mitt that two months on an uphill paper route earned you.*

I went outside in a holey t-shirt and pajama bottoms.

Mom was there. She was leaning out of the window the way I always did. That pleased me no end, that we had so much in common, even our secret pleasures.

I stood watching her for a while. She didn't know I was there and she was sort of moaning and talking to herself. It was in Greek and I don't know Greek except bad words like *skata*. For some reason the mask of Death came floating to the top of my mind. I choked it back but I must have cried out, because she saw me then. She said something to me, so softly I had to strain to hear anything above the patter of the train. I crept up closer to her.

She smelt sweet, like old oranges.

There was a full moon and it turned up the contrast on her, so her hair was like liquid coal and her face like chalk and her eyes like onyxes polished into cabochons. I could see her figure through the nightgown and I remember it was really firm and strong-looking, not like a forty-year-old woman's at all.

"It's time for me to tell you the family secret, Jody sweetheart," she said, so faintly that it was almost an overtone of the wind that the train made, "and about myths and truths."

"Sure, shoot," I said. I thought she just needed a quiet listener who wouldn't bug her; and I was good at that. Her husband was dying and I knew how it was.

Also, I was scared stiff and I was ready to listen to any kind of voice at all.

"Do you know why we went to Greece?"

"Sure," I said. "To see grandma and grandpa and the other Vlacha-pouloses and . . . well . . ." Jesus. I thought of the sky falling from the sky and the blue that was bluer than blue and I knew that was the real reason for me but I wouldn't ever be able to talk about it, not even with her.

"There was another reason," she said. "Okay. A lot of people think myths are just stories. They are, mostly—but they all come from some-where. Did you know that my family claims descent from the royal house of Admetos?"

Suddenly I could hear my own heart pounding above the train-roar, suddenly I knew I was shaking all over and—

She was saying, "It's not like in Euripides. That's just a distorted memory of the truth. There were things called Mysteries that only ini-tiates knew about in those days, mostly mumbo-jumbo about symbolic death and rebirth; well, I'm a Priestess of the Mysteries."

"Dad said you were a witch!" I blurted out.

She laughed very lightly and I couldn't tell if it wasn't the rattle of a chain in the train or the clang of a distant shutter . . . "Sure, baby. Italians are very superstitious."

She touched my cheek and her hand was icecold. Or maybe I was burning with fear.

I heard her say: "Our family . . . and that includes *you*, and that's why you have to know this, because I'm going to go away, soon—" *I'm not hearing this* I thought *I'm not I'm not* "—our family has the blood of Admetos in its veins, we all have the power to cheat Death, to trade places with other people . . . because we understand Death. You can see Death whenever you want to, Jody, whenever you look into a mir-ror and stare, past your own face, into the face within . . . well, I've decided to do it."

"Dad'll never let you!" I said fiercely. "Admetos was an asshole! Nobody would let the person they love commit suicide—" And I didn't believe it. I *couldn't* believe it.

And underneath I knew it was true as the blue of the sky over the Cape of Sounion, as true as the mask of Death, as true as the morning mist that tendriled the broken columns at Delphi . . .

Yah. I'd stared at mirrors before. I knew I carried Death inside me and I could will myself to face it. I knew that there were secret words that lay in my unconscious, spells that I could use. If the moment came.

I could hear her talking through the tumble of my heartbeat. She was saying how they'd made a mutual decision and how it was better for the kids otherwise she couldn't afford to send them to college on her earnings as a secretary—

She went on talking but it was the chattering of the train like teeth death rattle of wheels iron on iron chittering of unoiled chains thunder of the wind scream dinning in my head—

I made it to the cabin. I slid the door with a slam. I listened to myself breathing. Slower. Slower. Remote.

How could you do it, Dad? I wanted to bawl like a baby and nothing came. I glanced up and the mirror glared back, taunting. I turned to face the wall and it was metal and I saw my eyes reflected like ghost eyes eyes of Death and I squeezed them shut to shut off the eyes and plastered the blanket over my face and lay suffocating in the dark for the whole night, I couldn't sleep because I knew I'd dream and the mask would come for me—

Morning broke all at once. We were pushing through mountains and the train kept jerking to a halt and hauling slowly, off-rhythm . . . I found I'd been hugging my baseball glove like a teddy bear.

I took Sophie over to the dining car. We passed the parents' cabin and I walked very quickly. They'd opened the windows and the air smelled of drifting leaves and cold showers. We found a table with a white starchy tablecloth and a plastic vase with a pink rose, half wilted.

I was facing the wrong way and I was uneasy. But I tried to pretend like there was nothing wrong. For Sophie's sake.

"*Zwei Apfelsaft*," I said to the waiter. "*Spiegeleier. Speck.*" I pointed to the places on the menu, worn as an old papyrus under the slimy plastic cover, because I knew I'd pronounced it all wrong.

The waiter mumbled something I didn't catch. *Ah well,* I thought airily, *he has an Austrian accent.* The train was running more smoothly now; a soft pink dawn played over us across the rose-tinted peaks . . .

I saw Dad in the doorway. A smell of stale apples . . . He stood there without moving. The coat was gone. He was wearing fresh clothes. Something was wrong.

"Dad—"

"Jesus, Mary, and Joseph," he said—not in the funny accent—"she's done it, I can't think—" He started crying. I'd never heard that before. It didn't sound real. It sounded like the squeaking of the train wheels—

I got up. I was angry. I was hot all over. I stomped over to him. He looked healthy as hell and I thought his crying was phony and I wished he were dead. He was an asshole just like in the play. I stared up at him and I knew I was scaring him.

"I don't know how you managed to do it," I said. Quietly. "I used to think you were God sometimes, you with your clever colorful phrases and all. But you made her die. Maybe you can live with it. Fuck you."

He'd stopped crying now and his eyes looked like stone. He just gaped at me. "Ragazzo," he said, "God damn it, we need each other now. We made a logical decision, it was all for you kids, we weren't thinking about anything else. Christ, do you think I feel supercool about this or something?"

"Why should I comfort you? I'm your kid, not your mother!" I yelled. Then I pushed past him and went running to their cabin and pulled the door open.

Their cabin was a mirror image of mine; they made them back to back to save on rivets. The walls were metal like ours. The bunks—

I saw her on the lower bunk. She wasn't dead yet. She was still breathing. But something had gone from her. Even though it was broad daylight now the contrast was still turned up on her, as though a different light, a moon-drenched pale light, shone over her . . .

The white face hid a hint of sky blue.

"Mom," I whispered.

I bent over to kiss the closed eyes. I felt them tremble a little. Then I turned around and saw the mirror over the basin—

You know how in the old days they stuck a mirror over your face to see if you were still alive? They're always doing that in Sherlock Holmes movies . . .

—breath stains frosting the glass so I could only just see my own face blurring and melting—

(Behind the frost, the train purred past mountains softly furred with green. The brightness hurt. I went and closed the shutters.)

I stared into the mirror. I stared at it angry, because I'd never been angrier in my life. Dad had done the wrong thing. You don't let people die in your place. I wasn't thinking about our family's future and how hard they must have fought over it. I just knew it was wrong.

—the frosting shifted, unfocused, shifted—

My own irises through the mist. Alien. Cold.

I knew she was going fast. In a few hours the spell would be one way. And I was starting to know other things too. I was starting to remember things. Words were welling up behind the dam of my unconscious.

Things I had known all the time.

I hurled all the anger I could dredge up at those eyes. I was going to pull her out of there. My eyes stared back, concentrating my anger.

"Come and get me!" I screamed and the thing inside me leapt clear of me and fell swirling down the irises that spun and twisted and there were tunnels and tunnels and they were skull eyes walled by patches of white bone graying into terrible blackness—

Cold. Cold.

Faintly the train rumbled still.

I guess each person has his own private death. All the images and things he's most afraid of, everything he's pushed down to the very bottom of his mind—

Cold and darkness.

Then cold and light; moonlight without a moon, and I saw I was in a spotlight walking on a field of springy skulls, as though each one were attached to a bedspring, bobbing up and down as I trod. It was an eerie bouncy smoothness . . .

Then a voice that came from all around me. In a language I didn't know. But I understood it perfectly:

Who art thou, that darest enter?

The voice was echoshifted so I couldn't tell where it came from, it sprang out of the darkness and it made a cold wind with a whiff of methane and rotten egg gas. I suddenly knew the answer to that question, and I spoke a stream of gibberish that sounded like this *gispesimikyeuranuasterondos* and I knew it was Greek: *I am a child of earth and of starry heaven.*

It came out in a blurry kind of way and I was trying to stop myself from bawling or screaming or wetting myself, it was that bad. It was a tall deep darkness and I knew it stretched to forever. The voice asked more questions and I answered in the same gibberish and sometimes I knew what it meant but sometimes I didn't and it went on for it seemed like hours—

Then *bam!* A flight of stairs in the spotlight and banisters with bony fingers quivering and cobwebs and I walked up it. My own steps. Ping.

Ping. Metallic, distant. And the heartbeat. And so far away it was almost like sea waves lapping—the kettledrum of train on mountainside . . .

I was scared. Shitless. But I was so angry. There was something fake about all this. It was too plastic, too like a horror movie. I knew I had to walk up the steps and I did, and the lightpatch grew a little and there was the music of harps, dry and dissipating quickly into the dusty darkness.

"So you like my show?" A low voice inside my head.

I saw him. The skull face. And purple tights and a green cape and the Greek letter *theta* in a circle on his chest.

He was standing on a landing on a kind of mezzanine and the harp players were at his feet and they were skeletons and harps of bone with prows of ghoul faces and red crystal eyes. And a low wind moaning. And a chorus sighing. And a string orchestra, sort of a sneering, trilling ostinato of high-pitched squeaks . . .

"I asked you a question, kid."

"I think it's . . ." What did you say to Death? "I think it's phony, damn it! Give me my mother back!"

There. I'd said it. Now he'd take me and I'd live down here forever.

"Well, well, well," said Death. A grin widened and faded out. "I've seen a lot of people like you . . . selfish people, the lot of you. Always wanting something. Preferably for nothing."

"I can pay!" I said. "You can come and get me instead! I'm from the blood of Admetos and the bargain stands still, the bargain you made with him—"

"Don't give me that shit," said Death. "I'll do whatever I please." But he was shaking. Maybe there *was* a chink in his armor.

I looked him over. I was scared, sure, but somehow not as badly as I thought I'd be. I was more scared when I didn't know what to expect . . . the music and the skulls were spooky but plastic. "So bring her back to life."

"God, you're insufferable!" he said, then he did a hideous cackle. I'd been expecting one for a while, so I stood firm and didn't let it faze me. "If I let her go now, I'm still going to have to collect sometime, you know that. Besides, I don't bargain. It's a fixed price store here."

"Heracles didn't think that when he wrestled you to the ground."

"I'd like to see you try."

I stood and listened to the wind. The wind howled but I didn't feel anything. It was dry and cold. When I spoke the air frosted. As I watched him he shimmered and changed into the actor at Epidauros with the mask of death. It was like the nightmare, close up. The skull face was dead white and the eyes were dead and I couldn't read them . . .

"Okay," said Death. "If you're going to stand there forever, I suppose we might work out a little something. I don't get much amusement here. I don't suppose you wrestle, but—how about something else?"

"I thought I was just supposed to stay here and you would go wake her up," I said slowly.

The cackle came again. I wasn't afraid anymore. I was in this and I was going to fight it out till the end.

"I love children," he said. "They're so illogical. You won't be around to enjoy her if you die, will you? What would be the point? Oh, don't give me that bull about love and compassion. I don't understand things like that. They don't pay me for my empathy quotient. Anyhow, if you stay here, when your sister grows up she'll come looking for you. She's got the power too, you know. And she adores you."

"How do you know?" Suddenly I felt proud of Sophie. As I'd never done before. I thought of her without me and—

"Play chess?" he said suddenly.

"You saw *The Seventh Seal?*" Mom and Dad always made me watch the serious movies on channel 26. (*Expand your experiential cosmos*—)

"Shit yes. I always watch every movie where I'm the big hero."

"The way I interpreted it you were more like the bad guy. Anyways, I don't play chess."

". . . Monopoly?"

"Uh uh."

"Too bad." He started to shimmer again, as though to change shape, then changed his mind and stayed as the play actor. . . . "I've got it! This dude called Orpheus came by once, and . . . you sing?"

"Oh sure. I tried out for the Brooklyn Boys Chorus and I shattered a 69¢ Burger King glass."

"Oh, get out of here," said Death.

"Baseball?" I said faintly . . . and tried to choke it back but I knew I'd said it and I was in for it now and as if to play up my helplessness the music of strings and harp welled up and the moan of the wind shrilled to a shriek—

"That's it!" said Death briskly. He clapped his hands. Suddenly I saw that we were overlooking a field of plastic-looking grass and that there were tiers and tiers of spectators and the train rumbling suddenly turned into the murmur of a crowd—

"I'll put your mother on third base," he said. I saw her there. She stood still like a statue and even at the distance I could see how beautiful she was and how the light on her was still moonlight even under the gathering sunlight that was breaking overhead and the sun was yellow and had eyes and a frown like in a kid's painting. "I'll put your dad on first; he's got farther to go because after all he started it all. Now all you have to do is . . ."

He took off his mask.

It was Chet Perkins, the Pumpkin. Handing me the expensive bat I'd carried with me across Europe and hadn't used once.

I looked at his slits of eyes squinting at me and his body shaking like a jello that's been left out too long and I hated him. He shimmered back into his superhero costume but now it was topped by a green and purple baseball cap with the big *theta* on it. Theta for *thanatos*. The skull face scrutinized me. I saw right through the eyes into the old landing with the ghouls playing harps and I knew that our pavilion overlooking the baseball was a fakery on top of a fakery.

Then I turned around and looked at the field and the crowd screaming began to make me feel funny and warm inside and I knew I wanted to do whatever it was, even if I died trying . . .

I felt Death's breath in my back. Cold and slimy.

"Okay, ragazzo," he said, and he suddenly sounded like my dad and made me twist my intestines . . . "All you have to do is hit a home run. And I'm pitching."

I gripped the bat and started walking down the steps, I could see that it was like five hundred steps down to the grass below and the sun was hurting my eyes—

Death called after me: "How about second base? Did you have anyone in mind?"

"No," I said, not looking back. I didn't even want to think about it. Aunt Rosie? Poor old Grandad who died of a surfeit of booze? I tried to push the thought back as far as I could. I took three more steps and I heard Death taunting me.

"You humans are all alike!" he cackled. "Selfish, selfish, selfish. Just think what's in your power! You could bring back anyone to life— Jesus Christ, Einstein, Shakespeare—"

I turned around. "Damn it, I don't give a shit about those people! I'm just a kid who wants his family to stay in one piece!"

"Charity begins at home, eh?"

"Fuck you!"

I sort of came to. I saw the tiers all around stretching as far as I could see but sometimes there were holes in the tiers and I saw blackness through them lanced by eerie light. They were like living backcloth, in a seedy off-off-Broadway theater or something, that hadn't been used in a long long time.

I was holding the bat, my own bat, and it was a little-league-sized field so I saw Death in his supercostume standing pretty near and licking his chops.

"Where's the catcher?" I yelled.

Death vanished. I swirled round. He stood behind me and I got a whiff of his foul breath as he burst into a villainous campy laugh. "You could do with a good mouthwash," I said. Then I hefted the bat and waited. The crowd's murmur was the same as the pounding of the train . . . the tiers of living people started flapping so I knew it was all a backcloth now. And a wind gusted through the gaps, icy and fetid as Death himself.

I wanted to go find the locker room and scrub myself into pieces before I came on. But I was there and the crowd was screaming and I saw Mom and Dad, but I saw right through them too so I knew they were shades of people, and the sun shone fierce as anything making me blink over and over and it was cold as anything . . .

Chet Perkins was up there doing his fancy warm up and—

Zing!

Talk about a fast ball. I was still waiting for it when I heard the *s-s-t-r-r-r-i-ke ONE!*

I knew it was all a set up now. I knew it was going to be a dirty game all the way.

Death vanished and popped up all over the field, here an outfielder there a short stop, and then he'd guffaw and snicker and giggle and the crowd up there would copy him. I looked closer at the crowd and saw they were all—

Ghosts. Zombies. Headless torsos. Withered shrouds with gargoyle faces. Eye sockets dripping rheum.

It's hopeless, I thought. "God damn it, you've got all the cards," I yelled at Death, who was still in the form of the Pumpkin. "You can make the ball travel faster than light or something and you can rig up this whole Halloween charade to gross me out and give me the creeps . . ."

"Oh, it's a slow ball you want, huh?"

He pitched.

I waited.

Slow motion. Crowd shrieks dropping an octave like a 78 burbling to a 45 now to 33 now a heart-thump below the threshold of hearing—

The ball hung there for a moment and I saw it was moving dancing in the sunlight, it did three quick figure-eights and somersaulted into swooping sweeping curves and zigzagged like a hummingbird, hypnotizing me, and then it dangled in front of me—

I swung and it dodged and I swung and it dodged me and then it whooshed right past me into the strike zone and I was still swinging at nothing—

Thwack! Second strike.

Okay. I'd had it. I didn't want to play anymore.

"Okay, Death," I said.

Laughter pealed like funeral bells. "Ha! You can't take it, can you! Well," Death said, stalking towards me, "I let this go on because I wanted to teach you a lesson. You can't win! I am the great leveller, the ultimate nothing in everyone's life! I am totally fair! You can't cheat me!" He was towering over me and his cape was flapping and I saw the scythe sprout out of his bony hand. "I represent justice! Justice!" he shouted. "Everyone dies! Everyone! Everyone!" Holes of eyes burning blackness—

I dropped my bat and stomped towards him in a rage. "If you're so fair how come you don't die yourself, huh?" I screamed. "You're just a God damn hypocrite! Yah! Jesus!"

He stopped cold.

He turned his back on me and walked over and plucked a baseball out of the air. "Have it your way," he said.

He pitched this pathetic pitch that a first-grader could have handled with a plastic bat. . . .

I felt the thunk as I lashed out and then I sprinted without thinking at all and Death just stood there without stopping me. I saw the ball fly through a hole in the big canvas crowd and I ran and ran and my mom reached home plate and vanished and my dad was puffing like crazy with his fur coat flying and he reached it too I didn't stop I ran I ran

I looked up.

On the staircase in the darkness with the harps and wailing strings and the skeletons strumming . . .

Death in his superhero costume on his throne.

I stood panting for a while. Then, "Why'd you let me win?"

Rumble. Rumble. The train.

"I don't have to justify myself!" Death grated. Then he looked down and I tried to stare him down but he wouldn't even look at me.

God, I needed a shower!

I said, slowly, "All this crap about justice and the grim reaper and all . . . all these ghostly sighings and gibbering skeletons and stuff like that . . . it's not real, is it? You're quite a softie, after all."

He didn't answer. I knew he'd never admit it.

Then I said, "I know why you're so bitter. I can see it so clearly. You want to die so badly but you can't! You have to sit here forever, collecting due debts, like an IRS man or a mafia beater-upper . . . You're jealous, aren't you?"

He still didn't say anything.

So I walked up to him and touched him lightly on the face. Although it was a skull it felt dry, like skin. And cold. But there was no quiver of breathing. Nothing.

"Gosh," I said, "I wish I could help."

Everyone has his own personal Death locked up inside him. I knew this Death; he was part of me and he belonged to me. But I had thrown him into the deepest dungeon of my soul. Of course he was bitter.

"I guess I'll have to try to love you, even when it hurts," I said. "After all, I love my dad even when he farts up such a stink I can't breathe."

"Will you get out of here, already?"

I fell up the irises and the light swirled and I stepped into the mirror—

Dad and Mom on the bunk. Sophie on Dad's lap. Daylight. A family album portrait . . .

Dad said, "Wow, son."

I smiled sheepishly at the three of them.

"It's going to be Paris in an hour and we're staying in a hotel on the Champs-Elysées," Sophie babbled, "and guess what there's a McDonald's on the Champs-Elysées right near the FDR Subway, Daddy says so—"

"*Oh Child of Earth and Starry Heaven!*" Mom whispered. I knew them for the words of the ancient ritual of rebirth, words from the Sacred Mysteries . . .

I was too empty to say much and I knew they were all too emotional to say anything sensible, they'd either all start blabbing or we'd be hugging each other in pieces and I couldn't stand a scene like that, not now.

Dad said, sententiously, "Isn't it true that there are those for whom the climax of their lives was a home run in Little League, and that's all they reminisce about to their grandkids for the rest of their lives?"

I took the hint. I'd done an incredible thing—though I wasn't at all sure how I'd brought it off—but now it was time to go on.

"Yeah, Dad," I said.

"*E finita la commedia, ragazzo mio, no?*"

"Cut the wop shit, *babbino.*"

I slipped out as quickly as was decent and went to watch the fields unreel.

Tomorrow Mourning

BY
NICHOLAS V. YERMAKOV

Philip had thawed.

Twenty-five years ago, I had killed him and now the resurrection jarred me. It brought to life feelings I had sought to murder long ago. I tried to picture him, the same thin, shy, beautiful boy with the nervous smile and the thick black hair. My own hair, which he had loved to run his fingers through, was now cut short and streaked with gray. My vanity had kept me from restoring its original color and now I was too set in my ways to change it. Even for him.

I tried to remember the girl he had loved. What was she like? I graphed the photo from my first novel. I hadn't looked at it in years. And there she was, standing in the staging area, a spectral twin in reverse Dorian Gray.

She had tombstones in her eyes. So young, so very young, yet such a tragic, empty look. Her hair was long and brown and streaked with highlights put there by an artful stylist. Her face was full and round, her nose just slightly upturned, her lips curved gently in an expression that bordered on a pout. The legs were thin and not especially well shaped. They were legs and that was all that could be said for them. Her hips were slightly larger than the rest of her and there was a small, soft roll of fat around her midsection. All of this had been carefully kept from the readers. For publication purposes, the photo had been cropped just below the shoulders. The many necklaces and amulets could be seen, as well as the beginning curve of breasts, though the framing was achieved so that their true size was not perceived. They were quite small. The idea had been to concentrate on what she had considered her best feature—the eyes.

I saw them now and they were blank. They spoke of walls and fences. They were heartbreaking. I looked at her, the girl that Philip loved, deciding that I didn't know her. I wondered just how many critics who had spoken of such things as "a tortured honesty of insight" and "her haunted visions" had been influenced by the sight of those eyes. Today, when I looked into the mirror, there had been no gravestones there. *That* look had disappeared a long time ago. I canceled out the holo.

A long time ago, I had shown him that book, my first, in order to impress him. Well, that had been part of it. The other part of it was that I had wanted him to know me. Twenty-five years ago and more, I had been under the illusion that one could know an artist from the work.

Twenty-five long years since he went into the freeze. Some fifteen novels later (or was it thirteen? I conveniently forget about the early, awkward ones), I was no longer a "starving artist." I tried to recall that time. I seemed to have had such purpose then. What a laugh. Back then, what did I know of purpose, who was bothered by the fact that most men did not even look twice at me? Well, that had changed, perhaps only because they knew me from the talk shows. There was no scarcity, now. Still, the "triumph" was a Pyrrhic victory. I could never truly be certain if a man was with me for myself, or for what I was—a famous author, a celebrity, a wealthy woman, a "catch." Being in my company was worth notoriety and I no longer trusted quite so easily, or so blindly. With Philip, I had known for certain. No, *she* had known for certain. And I didn't know her anymore.

The girl he had loved was a woman now. A different woman. Older, stronger, independent. Sure of herself. I didn't need him anymore. And, I realized, I wanted him desperately.

Killing him off, murdering the memories, had been so hard and brutal and it had taken so long that I thought I had effectively wiped the slate clean. How awkward and embarrassing to realize that I had been lying to myself all these years.

Vision of a younger girl, the one I didn't know anymore, dressed in filmy white chiffon that billowed in the wind. Standing high atop a lonely mountain, screaming out into the void. "Philip," she cries, "I hate you! You can't leave me, it's not fair!" There is no answer, Philip, of course, having been frozen against the possibility of a cure being found for . . . what was it he was dying of? Leukemia? That's right, how strange, I *had* almost forgotten that. Anyway, the vision continues. . . . Philip doesn't answer. He sleeps in frozen shimmering crystal, a bemused half smile on his face. The girl is maddened into frenzy. "How *dare* you do this to me?" Get ready, here comes the punishment to fit the crime: "I'll kill you for this, Philip! I'll kill you!" She breaks down and sobs, dramatically. "I'll forget you, that's what I'll do. I'll drive the memory of you out of my mind. That's what you'll get for leaving me, so there!" Fade out into the howling wind.

The chime sounded and I turned to face the staging area. My God, there he was. All dressed in white and looking weak and frail. Thinner. More pale. He looked as though he had been sick. Of course he did, what else was I expecting? I stuffed my fingers in my mouth to suppress an involuntary giggle. I managed to compose myself, then I keyed in the mike.

"Hello, Philip."

The holo's head moved, questioningly. "Felicia? Felicia, is that really you? You sound a little different. I can't see you."

He sounded just the same as I remembered him. "My projector's out of order," I lied.

"Oh, what a shame! I really wish that I could see you. They said that I could graph you today, so I took a chance. . . . You've moved."

"A while ago."

"The Hamptons. Very ritzy. Do you know, I've never been there?"

"Well, you'll have to come out soon and visit me. When are they going to let you out?"

"Tomorrow." *So soon?* "Felicia? Do you think . . . I mean, it would be nice if you could come and meet me. Can you get away?"

I nodded, then realized he couldn't see me. "Y-yes, of course I can. What time?"

"I'll see you around noon. I'll meet you in the garden, okay?"

"Okay."

"Well . . . 'by. Until tomorrow."

I couldn't bring myself to say those words to him again. "Until tomorrow, then." He shimmered out.

I looked down at my hands and saw that they were shaking.

I took the boom tube from East Hampton. Settled back in the thickly padded seat, I watched the scenery fly by at over two hundred miles per hour. I couldn't look for long, the tube's distortion and the blurring effect made me dizzy. I tried to read, but found that I was unable to concentrate. I allowed myself to drift along with my anxiety, not trying to fight it, merely accepting it and soon I began to calm down a bit. The stops fly by rapidly. Babylon . . . Rockville Centre . . . Valley Stream . . . Jamaica. I changed tubes and continued, at a somewhat slower pace, on into New York City.

The water in the East River was still dirty. Some things never change. The surface was choppy and covered with whitecaps. Several hovertugs were struggling with a tanker. I looked across, at Queens. A chill breeze blew through the UN gardens and there weren't many patients out today. It was too cold. The Secretariat Hospital loomed behind me, with the Hammerskjold Clinic, that once housed the General Assembly of the United Nations, off to one side. A different kind of healing was done here now. A healing which I felt was infinitely more successful. I was about to benefit from it. Or was I? It had been a long time before I was able to accept the fact that I would never see Philip again. I made him dead. Now, he was on his way to see me. What would I say to him?

The wind whipped over the river. A lonely seagull screamed by, dropping a mollusk onto the pavement below, where it shattered. The bird dove down to retrieve the remains.

"Felicia?"

A knot formed in my stomach. I had thought I would be ready, but the sound of his voice sliced through me like a knife. I was afraid to turn around.

"Felicia? Is that you?"

I closed my eyes and clenched my fists. I wasn't ready. I never should have come. I covered my face with my hands and turned around.

I spread my fingers, looking through them. It was as though the twenty-five years had never passed. For him, they hadn't. I don't know why it had such a strong effect on me, I thought the holo had prepared me, but it was different seeing him in the flesh. The wind made his hair stand up and his coat flapped like a sail.

"They gave these to me," he said, indicating the clothes. "This is really what they wear now?"

I couldn't think of anything to say.

"You don't have to worry about shocking me, Felicia," he said, softly. "I've seen pictures, even holos. I know what you look like now. I recognized you, didn't I?"

I removed my hands from my face and stared at him. He stared back. Neither of us said anything for long moments. I hadn't expected a slow motion sequence of two lovers floating blissfully through the misty air, settling into each other's arms. Nevertheless, it was unsettling. I wished I could have known what was going through his mind. Twenty-five years had passed for me. For Philip, it was like waking up from a long sleep. For Philip, this was only tomorrow morning.

I managed a tentative smile. "Did you sleep well?"

He grinned. "I dreamt a lot."

"Really? I didn't know that corpsi . . . ugh, I didn't know that you could dream. Do you remember any of them? Oh, God, will you listen to what I'm saying? Who could recall twenty-five years' worth of dreams?"

"I recall a lot of dreams," he said, shuffling his foot and staring down at the ground. Just like he always used to do, I thought. "I don't quite understand it, but they tell me it's probably because the mind has to have something to hold onto during all that time." He shrugged. "Want me to try and tell you some of them? I don't know if I can." His eyes met mine and I saw that he was frightened.

"Oh, Philip," I said, realizing that he was in my arms almost before I was finished saying it. It felt just like old times.

"I'm scared, Felicia, I'm so scared."

"I know, I know. It's all right. It's a scary situation."

We held each other tightly. My arms felt very firm around him. He was shivering.

"Felicia?" His voice was very soft, his lips close against my ear. "They didn't tell me. . . . Did you . . . are you married, now?"

He still sang in the shower.

It was a song that had been popular a long time ago, of course. It brought back some nostalgia, but mostly it made me wonder why I had ever liked it in the first place. Was my taste truly so sophomoric at one time?

We had gone to dinner together, at a place in the Village we used to like. The Twisted Stone was still there, in a basement off Christopher Street. It was not the same as Philip remembered it, having changed ownership several times over the years. As we walked the streets together, he kept remarking how things had changed, which puzzled me somewhat, for I had thought they still looked pretty much the same. After a while, he became strangely silent.

He said very little as we rode the boom tube back to East Hampton. The hospital staff had done their best to prepare him, but the accelerated effect of the future shock was beginning to take its toll. He looked lost. Confused. He held my hand, making absent caressing motions with his thumb. It was the way he had always held my hand, but it felt somehow different. I wasn't sure what it was.

When we were last together, it had been all that I could do to scrape together enough money to meet the rent on my half of the loft on Waverly Street. Now, he stared at my lodge, its pine wood weathered from exposure to the salt sea air so that it was no longer really blonde. I saw him taking in its wood and glass simplicity and I knew that he didn't see it the same way I did. For me, it was my house. My own statement of a return to a simpler way of life. For Philip, it was an elegant home, one which he was having difficulty placing me in. I could read all the emotions flickering across his face and I felt disturbed.

It was as I had feared. Too many years had gone by. We could not ever be as we once were. We had proven wrong the Zen koan. Tomorrow *does* come. It was here. It was now.

I bought a bottle of his favorite wine. It had once been *our* favorite wine, but my kidney condition dictated that I abstain from alcohol. I could have had a new one transplanted, but I rather liked the one I had and not drinking seemed a small enough price to pay to keep it. We sat by the hearth and talked. He told me many of his dreams. Some of them were horrible. A great many of them. I was shocked at the vividness of his recall, at the clarity of his descriptions. He had never been able to describe things so completely before.

"Were they *all* nightmares, like that?" I asked.

"Most were," he replied, slowly twirling his wine glass from side to side.

"What was it like, being a . . ."

"A corpsicle?" He smirked. "Relax, that word doesn't bother me.

That's all they called me at the hospital, ever since I came awake. They said I'd have to get used to it." A sad look came into his eyes. "I'm going to have to get used to a lot of things, I suppose. It might have been better had I died."

I put my arms around his neck and kissed him on the cheek. He smiled, pecked me back, hesitantly, then stretched out on the floor with his head in my lap. I played with his hair as he watched the ceiling and remembered.

"It's really hard to talk about, you know? I could make a bad joke, I guess, and say you really had to be there."

"I think I'll pass."

"Yeah, right." He chuckled, mirthlessly. There was a long silence. "I don't know," he said, "when it comes right down to it, I *can't* really talk about it. I can tell you about the dreams, all right, but any more than that, I can't. I just don't have anything to lock onto. You *really* had to be there."

"You don't have to talk about it, if it's painful for you."

"No, it's not like that. Pain really didn't have anything to do with it. There was no physical sensation at all. Did you ever have an operation?"

I nodded again, not mentioning that it was an abortion. The child that would have been, had it lived, his.

"Well, remember how they administered the anesthetic? The next thing you knew, the operation was over and there you were, groggy, asking when it would begin. In a way, it was something like that. Only, with one major difference."

I waited while he tried to marshall his thoughts. The vibrations of *déjà vu* were powerful within the room.

"I was really scared. I mean, more scared than I had ever been in my entire life. It was like I was going to die . . . only I wasn't going to die. I was going to go to a place called limbo. And there was no way anyone could prepare me for it. No one had ever come back from being a corpsicle before. They didn't even know if anyone would."

The muscles in his face were taut. He was still living through it. For him, it was only yesterday. I never should have asked. But then ignoring it was impossible for both of us. Twenty-five years had to be accounted for. They had to be confronted.

"I expected to feel cold," said Philip, after a while. "Instead, I merely went to sleep. The dreams, at first, were rather normal, whatever that may be. What I mean is, they weren't any different from dreams I'd had before. Hell, this is hard."

"It's okay," I whispered, bending to kiss his forehead. "Take your time." I realized, too late, what an awful thing that was to say, but he let it pass.

"Then, at some point, I don't know when, since I had absolutely no concept of time—it could have been seconds, minutes, days, or years—the dreams, well . . . they *changed*." He sighed, heavily. "In every dream that I had ever had before, I was always conscious of my body in some way. What I mean is, it was there with me, in the dream. I don't know, how can I describe what it's like, not having a body? I just can't. I didn't have one. It simply wasn't there. I wasn't even conscious, strictly speaking. To be poetic about it, I suppose that I could say that, for the first time in my life, I discovered that I had a soul."

He tried, haltingly, to continue, but the words simply wouldn't come. What he knew, what was now a part of him forever, was something that he would never be able to share with anyone. Except, perhaps, another such as himself. I felt so sad . . . so moved. He began to weep.

At first, the tears simply began to flow and he cried silently. Then, he began to sob. I held him tightly, rocking back and forth, tears streaming from my own eyes. I kissed him, tasting the salt of his tears mingled with mine.

We made love.

The fire in the hearth spent itself, till only glowing embers remained.

It's never like what you think it will be. Philip had been very hungry. What I remembered, what I had once thought of as passion, I now perceived as need. His mouth had been everywhere, devouring greedily, breathlessly. His love was hard and fast and . . . juvenile. He didn't talk to me. He said words, but he didn't talk to me. I wanted to hold him for just a little while, but it had been like trying to catch the wind.

I had pretended to go to sleep. I don't know why, perhaps I was just trying to escape. He lay awake all night, eyes wide and staring at the ceiling. He didn't move a muscle. He didn't make a sound. In the middle of the night, I looked at him, lying there amidst the crumpled sheets, and he looked dead. I wondered who he was. Why did I feel, later, when it rained, that he was like a child, come crawling to his mother to escape the terrifying sound of thunder?

I must have drifted off, sometime. In the morning, I found him in the kitchen, his omelette become scrambled eggs. He was stabbing at the pan with the look of a boy poking at a wriggling garter snake. I realized that he was going to burn the eggs, so I took over. Funny, that hadn't changed, either. All previous attempts of his to make me breakfast had been doomed to failure, also. *Déjà vu,* again. He poured two cups of coffee and put one beside me. He had no way of knowing that I no longer drank it with milk and sugar.

"I was looking at your bookshelves, before, when you were sleeping," he said. "You really *are* very famous, aren't you?"

"Oh, more than some and less than others, I expect."

"Oh, no, I would say you're really famous. Those quotations on your novels, all those people saying all those things about you. . . . And those photos of you, and the holos of you with all those famous people, I mean, I don't know who a lot of them are, of course, but I recognized one or two by name and the rest, well, I can tell they're really special."

I finished making the eggs and I served him. His eyes never left me. I sat down across from him to drink my coffee, which I no longer liked to drink that way. We appraised each other.

"It's really happened for you, hasn't it?" he said. "You've finally got what you've always wanted. Money, fame, success. . . ."

"It took a long time. And an awful lot of work."

"But you got it."

"Yes, I got it."

Long pause. He ate. I drank.

"Good," he said, finally. "I'm glad for you."

I didn't know what to say, so I thanked him.

"One of the nurses, in the hospital? She told me all about you." He took a monstrous mouthful and masticated furiously. "She's quite a fan of yours, you know. Always sees you on the talk shows." He chuckled. It sounded unnatural. "She asked me if I could get your autograph for her."

"Okay."

"I'm sure she'll really be thrilled."

"Is she pretty?"

"Well . . . yeah, I guess so, you could say she's pretty, I suppose."

"How often are you going to have to go back?"

He shrugged. "Who knows? They said to check in once a week, for a while, at any rate. It's all still pretty new, they want to keep tabs on all of us, just in case, you know?" He laughed, bitterly. "See, they're not sure. They've thawed out all the meat and they don't know if it'll spoil or not."

"That wasn't very funny."

He shrugged, again. He was the same. Totally the same. And yet
. . . and yet. . . . I felt a curious pressure in my chest. I couldn't tear
my eyes away from him. I felt as though I was trying to look through
him, as though I was searching for something, but I didn't know what
and I had no idea how to find it.

"What's the matter?" he asked.

"Nothing."

"You're looking at me funny."

"Am I? I'm sorry, I didn't mean to. I was only looking."

"It must be tough for you, huh?" He put down his fork and pushed
away his plate. "Things must have been going along pretty well for
you until I came back from the dead."

"What's that supposed to mean?"

"I don't know. I mean, I *do* know, but I don't know how to tell
you." He appeared to be trying to work himself, and me, up. For some
reason, it was necessary for him to become angry. I could guess what
that reason was. I was willing to let it happen.

"You feel left out, don't you?" I prompted him.

"No . . . yes. Yes, I feel left out, damn it! I don't know what's going
on with you! It's like . . . one minute, I'm away, then I'm back the
next and everything is different. You've had a whole life in that time.
A whole life!"

"I can't help that, Philip. I couldn't stop time."

"I know, I know, but that doesn't make things any easier. Sure, I
suppose I should be grateful that I'm still alive, that's terrific. I've got
another shot, now. But *look* at you! God, Felicia, you're more beautiful
now than you were twenty-five years ago. And I'm still the same. I
haven't changed. How the hell can I go on as if nothing's happened?
There were twenty-five years of your life that I've had absolutely nothing to do with! I don't know *anything* about that! What am I supposed
to do?"

I stared at him, evenly. "You could try getting off your ego, for
starters. That might help."

"Jesus Christ." He was stunned. "Jesus Christ, you *have* changed."
He shook his head.

"We all have to grow up sometime," I said. "You've got some
catching up to do."

"I don't know where to start."

"Right here, Philip. You start right here. To begin with, I know it
isn't easy for you, but then it hasn't exactly been easy for me, either. I
thought you were dead! For all those years, I mourned for you, without

even knowing it. I don't know what you think I did during all that time you were in the freeze, but the truth is I worked my ass off, and for a long time, I carried one king-sized torch for you. And I finally learned how to handle that and now you've returned and you seem to think that we can simply pick up where we left off, just like that. *We can't.*"

"What are you talking about? You think your age makes a difference to me?"

"I don't know, Philip. But I do get the feeling that when you look at me, you see your mother. The fact is, *your* age makes a difference to *me.*"

It stung him. And, predictably, he lashed out to get revenge, in exactly the manner I knew he would.

"It didn't seem to make a difference when we were in bed! You liked *that* well enough!"

"I like *you,* Philip. And I don't mind making love with you. It's very nice. But it isn't what I'm looking for."

The expression on his face was one of shock. I felt a little sorry for him. I would have felt still sorrier, only he was too busy feeling sorry for himself. My words . . . and time . . . had created a chasm between us. For a long time, neither one of us could cross it. Finally, he spoke.

"It's over, isn't it?"

I nodded, silently.

"It's actually over. I can't believe it. What made you . . . change?"

"Time," I answered. "It's been over for a long time, now. It was over that day, a long time ago, when I put down that torch. It was over by the East River, when the cold wind blew you back to me. I've outgrown you, Philip. I'm sorry."

"You're sorry," he repeated. "That's wonderful. Just wonderful. What am I supposed to do now?"

"What do you *want* to do, Philip?" I asked, quietly.

"I don't know."

"Well, let's find out. Okay?"

The Hashed Brown Buggy

BY
MARGARET ST. CLAIR

Elel woke from terrible dreams. All night long he had run through an underground maze from one danger point to another, tinkering with a leaky pump, fighting to clear out clogged pipes, erecting ineffective dams against a searching and corrosive flood.

In vain, in vain. The pump had failed; water or some heavier liquid lay in a broad sheet around its sump hole. The pipes had narrowed as he worked, had grown too narrow for even a drop to get through. The city wall crumbled. The dams shook, and the burning water poured in. All the transparent symbolism his mind had thrown up all night long to protect his failing body in its urgent need for sleep had been thrown up in vain.

His heart was pounding so hard that its beats shook the bed. Such dreams were murderous. Reality could be better forgotten awake than in such dreams. He must not sleep again.

On the wall a dim oblong showed the place of the big yellow-leaved calendar. He wasn't sure how long he had been here, but it was less than the span of a normal human life. They lasted better than he seemed likely to. But he still wondered how they could stand it. Thousands of them died every day, and they all foreknew death. Yet they went on working, breathing, hoping, rarely turned their hands against themselves. Brave and stupid. They never seemed to realize that madness would be their happiest ending.

Never mind, never mind. He still had something of a chance. Even if he couldn't get home—how easy all these repairs would have been at home where, with his own paradisial consciousness for his surgeon, his mechanic hands could have set all right—even if he couldn't get home, he might still be able to help himself. The buggy stood waiting by the curb. The girl horse must be standing docilely between the traces. It seemed to him he had felt a little better after his last foray. He would go.

His night shirt was soaked with sweat. He stripped it off and stood naked, trying not to cough or fall to the floor. He got a rust-colored coverall from the dresser and climbed into it. He might as well be neat and clean on this latest of his forays into what he thought of as the expanded present, the wider now.

He left the house. In the early gray light the buggy was standing beside the curb just as he had expected. The girls—horses—came to him through the House of Hermes. It always bothered him to use them, though they were perfectly willing, even eager, for it. But he knew they would not be good for much afterward. Only a great aim would justify him in this casual use of life.

Elel hesitated. He could send this girl home, and she would be none the worse for her adventure. She would not even remember it. But was not his own survival the highest morality? He had a sudden vision of the interior of his own ailing body, its deterioration no longer decently veiled in metaphor. His scruples left him. He untied the reins from the hitching post and sat down on the buggy seat.

The javelin was ready in the whip socket. It was a long, flexible lash with a cruel broader-pointed tip. All, even the whip stock, was blue-black.

He flicked the javelin. Its elegant arrow point whistled through the air. The horse girl started up obediently, trotting hard in place. A thread of sweat began to trickle down her sides. As she trotted, Elel could see a faint fog of power coming up from her diaphragm, curling around her shoulders, and meeting with two others from lower down.

Her legs were becoming a blur. Elel gave her a smart cut with the javelin, letting the point sting. Almost before she felt the lash she was off full tilt, away, away, the buggy rattling from her energy. Elel grabbed at the whip socket to steady himself.

They came back some time later. The horse girl was panting hard and running slowly. But another girl sat in the buggy seat beside Elel —a bird girl, fish girl, lizard girl—which one only it would be difficult to say. Were they scales or feathers that lay along her sides? Her integument seemed something she could doff at will, a parure, an adornment, an accessory. She had slanting silver-framed eyes, a slanting glance. She wasn't what Elel had meant to bring back with him, but then, he never brought back what he had meant.

The buggy stopped beside the small white house. The bird girl stood up. She stepped out of her plumage easily, leaving her vulval cleft delicately visible within a fine fluff of pubic hair. She seemed fully mammalian and human. Only in her armpits was there a hint of scales, or were they a daintily set, close-wrought imbrication of feathers? Elel thought of the plumage of a quail.

He got out of the buggy and helped the bird girl out. She smiled at him as she took his hand. Did he feel better? His notion of the time his forays took was always unsure. But it seemed to him that he hadn't coughed, or bled, or felt faint, for—oh—for more than an hour.

The horse looked up at them over her shoulder. Along her sides under the ribs had been at first a trickle of blood, but now it was a blur, a long rusty smear. Elel hesitated. The humane killer was behind the seat of the buggy, or should he put her out to pasture? She licked his hand and whimpered softly while he was trying to make up his mind.

The bird girl had almost learned how to talk during the journey back. She said, with only a hint of mewling, "I want to be St. Joan of Arc."

"That story has an unhappy ending, at least for her," Elel replied without blinking.

"I want it to have a happy ending," the fish girl said.

"What would that be?" he asked.

"That, when the faggots around the stake have been set on fire, a great storm should arise and put out the flames. That the heavens should be opened in glory. That she should be borne up alive to sit at the right hand of God."

"And after that?" Elel asked.

The fish girl was silent for an instant. Then she said, "After that, I want to be Cleopatra. She shall win the sea fight at Actium. She shall go on living with Antony. She shall be mistress of the world."

"Of the Roman world?"

"No, of course not. Of the world."

Elel said, "I could sell you to a sideshow. Or to a wealthy collector. It would help to pay for medical treatment. I have all sorts of markets for the things I bring back."

"You won't," the bird girl answered self-confidently. "And after that, I want to be Guinevere, no, Mumtaz Mahal."

"She died young."

"I'm not going to die young."

The horse had grown increasingly restless while they talked. The effect of the preparatory shot she had been given was wearing off. Her whimper changed to a whine, and then to a long keening howl. Her head jerked back and forth on her neck. She made swimming motions with her hands. A little white froth came out between her lips and ran down her chin.

Elel could wait no longer. The time to put her out to pasture was plainly past. He found the humane killer, cocked it, and let the horse girl have its bolt between her eyes.

She fell forward instantly, in a tangle of brown harness. The buggy moved a foot or two and then stopped. Elel worked the bit loose from her mouth, trying not to get blood on his hands. He must remember to wash the humane killer before his next trip.

The fish girl said, "Do you use one up every time you go out?"

"Most of the time, yes."

"And yet it doesn't do you any good."

He was silent, trying to explore his own body in the old, longed-for, healing way. Home seemed a luminous place of gods and demigods, tall and secure. She was waiting for him to answer. Finally he said, "I think I do feel better, though. As if I'd gained back a little lost ground."

The bird girl didn't pursue the topic. It was getting late. An after-sundown little breeze sprang up, turning over the leaves, paper trash and loose grit in the shallow gutter. She said, "I need some clothes."

"Grow them for yourself," Elel answered. He felt giddy, as if he were going to faint. He wanted to get inside and sit down.

"But you'll help me? Help me be who I want, I mean?" She leaned toward him questioningly in the gathering dusk. "It would be a diversion for you."

Her expectation was so patently out of line with his capabilities that it was flattering. Besides, if he did try to help her it might actually prove, as she said, a diversion. "Very well," he answered.

He stepped over the body of the horse and walked toward his front door. The house stood at the end of a dead-end street. It had been a packing shed once. The fish girl followed him.

He shut the door in her face. As soon as he was inside, he forgot her entirely. There was a lot of pain, a very bad pain, in his stomach. He turned on the light, got some water, and swallowed a pain pill. He had no trouble getting all the pain pills he wanted. The medical profession almost forced them on him.

But he mustn't go to sleep. He sat down on the narrow, unmade bed, his back against the white-plastered wall and his hands interlocked in his lap. After a minute he got a dull-pointed knife from a drawer, and, hunching forward, set the point under his chin.

He sat so most of the night. Once or twice he slept a little, brief blackouts, from which the knife point woke him before he could begin one of his panicky fugues through the interminable corridors of the underworld.

The night wore on. Grayness began to seep into the room from outside. Elel still sat motionless, unwilling to risk rousing the quiescent pain in his stomach by any sort of movement. But the pain came back by itself, and at last he got up, washed his face in cold water, and put on a clean coverall. He must have fainted while he was getting on the right leg of the garment, for he found himself on the concrete floor with a lump on his head.

Oh, how *boring* all this was! Painfully he got up, tremulously made his way to the front door and opened it. Last night's debris had been cleared away by somebody, silent and invisible hands. The fish girl was gone. Even the scraps of paper in the gutter had been tidied up.

The buggy stood ready beside the door. A new horse was harnessed to it. Another trip was possible. Once more Elel could explore the expanded present, the wider now. He might be lucky this time.

The new horse was a darling. Dark cloudy hair lay in delicious masses along her white, smooth shoulders. Her eyes were green, her breasts were round. And, despite the preparation she must have received, she looked up at him with a bright, eager, almost loving look. Her feet began to move even before he got in the buggy and touched the whip.

It was sad to think that when they came back, a few hours later, she would be so changed. There would be little ahead of her then except the humane killer which, sadly enough, he had after all forgotten to wash. He could put her out to pasture, of course. But he had been to that pasture once. The girls stood about, twitching their hides to keep off the flies. Sometimes a cooler wind would blow from a distant green field. The water was alkali.

He liked her too much, he couldn't do it. He got out of the buggy and loosed her from the traces to the accompaniment of a faint whimpering. "I'll take you back," he told her. "Somebody will come for you. You'll get home safe. It's all right." She still looked at him with the same, bright, eager, almost merry gaze.

He worked the bit out of her mouth. Did she feel disappointed? That must be his sentimentality. Her eyes were lowered. But she couldn't have been feeling much of anything.

Just as he took her by the hand, he had a private earthquake, a tiny but significant jarring and splintering along his bones. The thin partition he had erected between himself and his awareness bulged and broke. He couldn't not know what was happening.

Her hand shook in his. Perhaps he'd groaned. In all the world around him, she was the only object that seemed to promise any surcease. He began to caress her desperately.

Oh, this was better. She really was so pretty, a bit of earth's other face, its undeniable loveliness.

One of her arms kept getting in the way of his caresses. He lifted it away, and it fell back. A pretty arm. He put it out of the way twice more. Then he groped behind him for the javelin and slashed at the arm. He slapped a plaster over the stump.

The expression on her face had not changed. But now she was lopsided and rolled awkwardly when he tried to enter her. In the end, he had to push and lift her on to the buggy seat.

When it was over, he wept a little. He dusted off his knees. There were welts on them from the uneven wooden floor of the buggy. She had not made a sound. It seemed the ultimate profanation that he had to kill her with a dirty bolt.

He got up. He was sorry. But he did feel a little better. He'd noticed before that his contacts with these women helped him. He supposed she'd stay where she was, on the buggy seat, until they cleaned things up tonight.

He was about to go into the house for a pain pill when the bird girl came up. She was wearing a pair of bright red hot pants and a clinging shirt that seemed woven of dull aluminum.

"You're hard on them," she said, eyeing the dead horse on the seat.

"Where have you been?"

She shrugged. The small feathers at her ankles made her look a little like Hermes. Her long legs were as finely turned as those of his latest horse had been.

Elel felt a need to justify himself. "I was worth more than the girls," he said. And then, "If it was wrong, *they* should have stopped me."

The bird girl shrugged once more. A fly had begun to buzz around his dead lovely. "You got a little puff of vitality from them," she said. "But you'd have lasted longer without it. It left cracks in your bones."

"What do you mean by that?"

She put her right foot up on the buggy seat—she was wearing dark blue espadrilles—and scratched reflectively at her ankle. "Remissions, accompanied by striations," she said. "There's no use asking me to pull this thing for you, either. I'm no fool."

"I wasn't trying to hurt them! I didn't want to hurt them! I was, I was trying to—to get money for medical treatment. That's what I used the trips in the buggy for."

"All the medical treatment in the world . . ." she said, and laughed. "You're as good at justifying yourself as any human being would be. Surely you know that you contrived their deaths."

He didn't know whether to point out to her that he'd spared some of his horses—there were three or four, at least, in the pasture—or to accuse her of malice toward him because he hadn't helped her to be Guinevere. He closed his eyes for an instant. Then he reached behind himself for the javelin and made a viciously practical slash at her with it.

She'd moved. He missed. The motion unbalanced him. He leaned on the butt end of the whip for support. Uncomprehending, he saw the flesh of his arm crack open like a ripe pomegranate and the marrow roll out. It was greasy and gray.

He cried out. There was pain in his belly, pain in his bones. Human beings suffered so much, and, since his nervous system was finer than theirs, he was capable of suffering much more than they. He thought of that perfection of suffering that Dante had affirmed would be the lot of the damned after the resurrection and the end of the world.

He tried to say, "Why?" But no sound came out. The bird girl, who was watching him with her hands clasped behind her back, said as if she answered him, "It was one of those numerous nasty little experiments you yourself dreamed up. If you'd helped me have some happy endings . . ."

He didn't hear her. He fell forward heavily, and lay for quite a while kicking around in a circle like a poisoned coyote. But at last he was quiet. The angle of his neck showed that he had broken it.

The bird girl sighed. " 'He fell as a star falls,' " she quoted. She was silent for a moment. Then she looked over her shoulder toward the horizon, toward the clouds that always came up there at this time of day. "Let's put his head back on again," she suggested, "and see what he'll do next time."

Dancing in the Dark

BY
GLENN CHANG

"Vector, vector, QX nine nine four, repeat, nine nine four. Wolf, where are you?" The call rasped in my ears through an irritating fuzz-tone. My helmet-speakers had clipped out twenty-four hours ago, in the first big blowout, and since there were no spares available (I'd been out at the Auxiliary, tending LOBO, and they were all gone by the time I got back into Main A), I was suffering whenever anyone called. Lena's voice was nearly unrecognizable through the garbage on the beam.

I tongued on the mike. "Vector confirm, twenty-three latitude, Area G, bubble Zeta, that's Zebra Elephant Tallywhacker Arsebite." I knew I'd get heat from the operators for non-union call-letters if they heard me, but I didn't particularly care. There were bigger things to worry about than protocol in our present situation.

"Acknowledged. What are you doing, Wolf?"

"Sightseeing."

Silence. Uh-oh, I thought, she's worried again. A few seconds later her words confirmed it.

"Uh—want company?"

"Wouldn't mind it," I said.

"Okay. Be right there." And then she added, "Don't move," which tore it if she wanted to be obtuse about being Bedside Lena. I sighed but didn't answer, then settled back into the shape-fitting lounge-chair and contemplated the infinite.

Stars and darkness, jewels on black velvet . . . I reached out and spread one hand on the slick concave surface of the bubble, compelled to reassure myself. (Sure, only a centimeter thick, but it's top-grade space-glassalloy, prime-tempered, it won't crack. . . .) Below me in the infinite chasm was the bright glob of LOBO, my pet, my creation. It had been suspiciously silent in voice and alpha-numeric for the past twenty-four—ever since the Anomaly had cut out our mass-communications bands. It hadn't worried me at the outset, but now it did, for the tight-beam setup I'd been out rigging didn't work either. It wasn't general interference—the intra-Module systems still worked, but communication between habitats by radio was nonexistent. Commander DuTella was frantically working to set up a similar tight-beam to the others, after we found it worked with the Auxiliaries of this habitat. Except for LOBO.

"Ah, Wolfie-baby, there you are." I felt her hands slither around me through the monolayer of the suit, her voice coming in clearer by head-to-head contact. "You're cold. You all right?"

"Well as could be."

"Grump." The arms hugged closer; I felt her body press against me, fitting quite nicely. "Doctor says relax, Doctor."

"Uh-huh." I began to warm up. Thermal insulation in these suits was, of course, less than perfect, manufacturers' claims to the contrary. Right now I didn't mind it.

"Something on your mind?"

"Um," I said. "LOBO. He's playing the strong silent type."

"The Anomaly?"

"Has to be. He won't even answer me on Ears-Only." I tongued off my mike, turned to face her and told her to do the same by pointing and making a cut-off motion with my hand. She nodded and did so. "It's a channel we have for the private stuff," I explained. "Unauthorized, of course. But I found out a long time ago, don't let the bureaucrats know everything about what you've got to offer them."

"Space Operations has been pretty good to you," Lena said. "Better than to most."

"Sure," I said, "but they're still shacked up with the military. And you know how I feel about the military."

"All right," Lena said, giving up. "So what is with LOBO?"

"I really don't know. He just won't respond. His circuits are good; the check-points are all green. I know he's receiving. It's as if he were obstinately silent, or . . ." I faltered a bit, but finally said it "or catatonic."

"I see." Lena's voice was carefully neutral. "How are *you?*"

I shrugged. "All right."

"Good." She paused. "Unfortunate. About LOBO, I mean. We need him."

"Oh? Urgent?"

"They think so. The—Anomaly has been moving faster. Interference and background radiation building up."

"But they still don't know what it is."

She shrugged this time. "Colored lights, a conglomeration of ions and particles, an electromagnetic force-field . . . an Anomaly. But now they think it's guided by something. Maybe even conscious."

I looked at her over my shoulder. "You mean . . ." Then it hit me. "Then this—thing," I said slowly, "might be It." I pronounced the capital *I*.

"Right," Lena said.

I stared out at the revolving panorama as our floating world turned. Earth and Luna, the other bright pinpoints of the habitats, edged slowly into the field of vision, then away.

"Well, god damn," I said softly. "Then our first visitor—our first alien—is a bunch of particles. A wacky radio-map. A cosmic will-o'-the-wisp."

"Could be."

"But what else?" I held my hands palms upward. "Got to be."

Lena said nothing.

"If we could talk to it—" I began, then felt a flash of irritation. "Damn LOBO."

"DuTella wants to talk to you," Lena said.

"About what? I don't have time to jive with him. Tell him to keep up the good work with his Tinker Toys."

"Come on, Wolf. He's supported you and the LOBO project all along. He's willing to help you, not control you."

"So he says."

"You won't do any good down here. We need you on the Board."

"If LOBO is not talking," I said, "then the Board is useless. Not if any—"

But that was all I said that could be heard, because the tight-beam Ears-Only activated itself then, free of the cycle-hum and fuzz-tone.

"Wolf, Fenris, master lupus, I am dying, Egypt, dying. Oh western wind, where wilt thou blow. Into the valley of death I ride, boldly ride, but there is only shadow, and I cannot see your face." The voice was the toneless, precisely correct voice I'd synthesized for LOBO's auditory responses. That made it worse, and I felt a chill as LOBO continued to babble nonsense on the tight-beam.

"Wolf. Are you all right? Answer me." Lena's voice was suddenly anxious. She'd probably felt me stiffen up in shock and surprise.

"Hang on," I said. "I'm all right." I listened a bit more to LOBO's rantings. "I think," I said slowly then, "we'd better go back up to the Board."

The Boardroom was abustle with harried-looking technos and associate researchers—even the theoreticians were there, which somewhat surprised me—and the inimitable Commander Damien DuTella, tall, rail-thin, and stoic. The workers eyed me with wariness and respect when we drifted into the room. DuTella cast a glowering look in my direction.

"Well, here is our resident genius." His voice was sharp with tension. "Where've you been? We've been trying to find you for the past twelve hours."

"Forget it," I said to Lena. "See you later." I turned and made to go.

"Come *on*, Wolf." Lena held my arm, not hard, but I hesitated anyway. I looked at her. "All right," I said finally.

She led me closer to DuTella. "Wolf says," she announced, "that LOBO's talking again."

DuTella looked at me closely, and his expression seemed to reflect approval, though reluctantly. "Good," he said, sounding awkward. "Good. Can we then—"

"Wait a moment, Commander," I said. "Not so good. LOBO is talking, but he's not making much sense."

The approval vanished, and suspicion appeared on DuTella's face. "What does that mean? Can you fix that?"

I stifled an angry response. Instead I said, "I'm not sure. I'll need to work on it."

DuTella glanced at the Board, and at the people now studiously avoiding looking in our direction, humphed once, turned back to me, said, "Well, do it, then," turned again and stalked off to confer with several other uniformed guards near the doorway.

Lena and I looked at each other. I shrugged again and went to the Board. The technos made way for me, and I stood still and studied it for a moment. Floor to head-height, the breadth of the wall, the Board dominated this room. A techno stood to either side of me, poised at their respective keyboards. "Activate, synchronize, run tape," I told them, and they bowed to their tasks, urging the awesome data-massaging facilities of my brainchild out of dormancy and back to ready phase. While they worked I began manipulating the dials and levers and keyboard in front of me. I would set the Ears-Only channel onto general broadcast, and didn't want anyone to notice. The silly protocol

DuTella had instituted with multiple operators (which saved all of five or ten minutes before startup) would help. Plus they'd never know the difference if I interfaced it right.

In a few minutes I had it all rigged. I switched on the microphone and spoke. "LOBO, LOBO, this is Fenris, talk to me." I hit up the Respond codex on the keyboard and waited.

"Talk that talk, walk that walk. Half a league, half a league, half a league onward, and I will fear no evil because I'm with the meanest son of a bitch in the valley." I glanced to the sides and saw the technos look up at the speakers with surprise and astonishment. "Give me the beat to free my soul, I'm lost in this rock and roll, and drifting away. Where's the line, oh help me before I sink into the whirlpool. Whirlpool—Charybdis—Sampo. Note and investigate." I snapped to attention at the sudden return to clarity in LOBO's words. "Alien resonances—nonindigenous configurations—foreign wavelengths—xenophylogenous entity. Talk—communication—lexicon, Rosetta Stone, concordance, crash priority. Speak to me only with thine eyes, let us talk of shoes and ships and sealing wax. Strait is the gate, don't be late, dinner at eight, don't hesitate." And it was lost again into more nonsense.

Or was it?

I turned to the now substantial group of people gathered round the Board. "Uh," I began, "LOBO is a bit—confused. I mean, he's trying to tell us something."

"Like what?" DuTella had spun around at the amplified babblings and now strode across the room to confront me. "This doesn't make much sense to me."

"That's because you're not listening." I met DuTella's glare with one of my own. "Did you note that short space where he spoke normally?"

DuTella winced. "I wish, my dear Doctor Kohara, you would stop calling it a *he*. That thing—"

"Is my creation," I interrupted, "and I'll call it anything I want."

Lena came to the rescue as always. "Calm down, both of you. What do you mean, Wolf? What's LOBO saying?"

"I think," I said slowly, "he's in contact with the Anomaly. Or, more likely, the Anomaly has taken him over."

Everyone looked at me quizzically.

"I know, it's hard to understand. Let me explain." I chose my words carefully. "LOBO is my brainchild. I built him. I conceived him. And, in the final analysis, I understand him. This Board"—I made a sweeping gesture with my arm—"and that Auxiliary out there, are merely the life-sustaining machinery for LOBO, as our bodies are the same for us. You see?" Their expressions didn't brighten any. "Look. The electromagnetic configurations sustained by all this hardware are LOBO. I won't argue whether he's alive—that's mere philosophy. I will assert that he is as sentient, or conscious, as any artificial-intelligence construct that we've ever tried to build. Grant me that." No one denied it. "Okay. Now LOBO has certain idiosyncrasies, thought-patterns"—I saw DuTella wince again, but I ignored it—"certain modes of behavior. He's mathematically and algorithmically complicated, but the data-massage takes care of that. In a word, he has a unique character, beyond the usual log-lan response of machine computation. And since I built him, since I programmed him, there are unavoidable similarities. Therefore I understand him best. Got that?" I saw their faces begin to show comprehension. "So I would know, best of anyone else here, what he was saying. Right?" I didn't wait for approval. "Because I know LOBO. I can read between the lines. And what I'm reading now is this. In some way the Anomaly has taken over his—senses is the best way to put it. It's been trying to talk to him. But—" I raised a finger in emphasis. "It's alien. Utterly alien. And machine or no, the only other sentient beings LOBO has been in contact with are us. So of course this contact is, at best, disturbing. At worst"—I hesitated again—"it could drive LOBO into psychosis, madness—"

"I'm not sure I can believe this," DuTella said.

"You got anything else better?" I demanded. DuTella didn't answer. "It can't help being biased," I went on. "We made it. It's got to be like us. Like me," I corrected myself. "Fenris. LOBO is Fenris, Fenris is LOBO. Simple as that."

"So what can you do then, with a—psychotic machine?" DuTella said grudgingly.

"Try to heal it," I said softly, looking sidelong at Lena. "Then we can worry about talking to our new neighbor."

The Anomaly had appeared in our sky for the first time a month ago. They'd thought it first a glitch, a bad wafer in the circuitry that turned up a singularly large concentration of electromagnetic radiation and particle emission in the direction of Orion. As time progressed and independent observations became known, the reality of its existence was confirmed. Something was out there. But what?

As if in answer, it began moving, toward the Sun. More exploration turned up inconsistencies. It was discrete, coherent radiation—but diffuse, with almost no mass. There was particle emission around its edges, generation of helium and higher elements—primitive nucleo-synthesis on a miniature scale. But it was too small for that to happen, according to the usual theories. Where was the mass that would keep it coherent, that held those particles and atoms together? The theoreticians went crazy trying to figure it out. And all the while it kept coming closer.

Then it changed course just outside Mars's mean orbit and headed toward Earth—and also increased its velocity. That was when they began thinking it wasn't exactly a natural phenomenon. Doppler measurements on particle emissions pegged its approach at about a thousand kilometers an hour. Sixty thousand kilometers away from the habitats it suddenly slowed to a sedate several hundred, then came to a virtual dead stop. That had been seventy-two hours ago. Two days later all inter-habitat and trans-Earth communications lines were jammed. Each of the floating worlds—artificial and natural—was isolated, cut off from the others. That wasn't so bad. What was, was the apprehension it generated, if the mood here in Module Primus was any indication, that could easily turn into panic. No one knew what the Anomaly was or what it wanted—nor was anyone prepared to deal with whatever it did next.

It was somewhat ironic, too, that Wolf Kohara and his toy, out of all the rather awesome facilities out here in Earth orbit or stable libration, was the key connection to whatever that thing was that came to be called the Anomaly.

Or had been until LOBO had gone catatonic, then psychotic. Like father, like son, I thought with some unease as I listened to more of LOBO's babbling.

"Just like the bringdown with me," I said to Lena. We stood close together by the Board. Only a few technos were around, but we whispered so as not to be overheard. "We've the same psychological makeup, LOBO and I."

Lena looked at me and saw I was serious. "Well and good," she said slowly. "But you were a special case, Wolf. We knew each other so well—you, me, Carla. Because of that, I could pull you out. Even so, it was the hardest case I ever had in my life. I'm not sure I can do it again."

"Just do the same thing. It worked then, it should work now."

"Recuperative psychotherapy," Lena began patiently, "is not some pill you can take to make a headache go away."

"I'll help, don't worry. I'm right here, and I'll cue you if things start going bonkers."

Lena made an exasperated sound. "If what you say is right, Wolf, then that th—I mean, LOBO has been jolted out of his reality-continuum: the safe humans-only universe he's known up till now. If that's now been thrown out by the Anomaly—"

"My world went the same route when Carla died," I said. "And here I am."

Lena only looked at me silently, biting her lip.

"Don't sell yourself short, Doctor," I said. "Come on. Let's give it a try."

She sighed. "All right. When do we cut in?"

"Give me the words and I'll code it."

"Try to get his attention. To make him stop a moment."

I nodded and bent to the mike.

"LOBO," I said. "This is Fenris. Read the voice-print to confirm. It's the big C, LOBO, the big C." I wiated. The babbling went on.

I turned to Lena. "He's not—" I began, then suddenly noticed it was quiet except for station background noise. The other technos looked around, at each other, at Lena and me.

"Okay," I said. "He's at ready." I stepped back and indicated the keyboard and mike. "Print or audio, it's all yours."

Lena bent to the mike, glancing quickly back at me once, then flipped it to send. "LOBO, this is Lena, a friend. Can you hear me, LOBO?"

"Friend?" Where had that inflection come from? I hadn't programmed them in. "LOBO-friend, Fenris-friend, earth-friend, light-friend, dark-friend—"

"LOBO-friend and Fenris-friend," Lena said hastily. "You are troubled. You have worries—problems. I sympathize with you. Tell me what ails you. What is wrong? Tell me how you feel." Her voice was low, soothing, solid, as she deliberately tried to set a calming mood.

"He doesn't understand inflections," I whispered, "Because—" But her look stopped me.

"Go ahead," she said to LOBO in that same voice. "Tell me."

"Dark," LOBO said. "Dark and nothing earthlight. Stars begotten, benumbed in shadow. There is no balance. I cannot hold your hand. Oh let me out of this nothing, endless nothing, for the dark is a beast whose face is—"

"Be calm, LOBO. Relax." Lena didn't change her tone. "Just talk. We'll listen. We're here. You're not alone, LOBO. We'll listen."

"You will listen? You are really there?" I felt dumbfounded listening to the voice of my LOBO. A *voice*, not a synthesized aural response.

"Yes. We're here."

And on and on it went. Lena at the mike, myself at the Auxiliaries, a slowly gathering crowd of onlookers about us. It got dicey in spots—*can* a machine go bonkers?—so I cut the audio and piped it into outlets we could plug into our ears. Now and then Lena looked at me and gave me a brave, if somewhat harried, smile. Not because the controls were difficult—she was nearly as adept on the Board as I—but because she'd reached out and brought someone back from that darkness once already. Namely, me.

And doing it again, with an artificial entity that nevertheless was the hand-made avatar of myself, as much a copy of myself as anything could be made, could have only been at least as much repeated hell. I could only marvel and salute her.

More time passed. It stretched out until it lost its meaning. I wasn't even aware of anything, after a while, except the Board, Lena's efforts, and LOBO's voice. And I learned things about LOBO. He cried. He laughed. He screamed in terror, lashed out in confusion and anger, lamented in travail. He did all these things—these human things, emotions, that I had never programmed in.

On one level I was secretly gratified. Project LOBO was proving itself: true artificial intelligence. And *sentience*. On other levels I was apprehensive. Space Operations and its big mama, the military, would now be hankering for the big payoff and the delivery of LOBO into their hot little paws. And more, even beyond the mundane: it had taken this, the Anomaly, to break through the last barrier. What was it —and what else could it do?

"Wolf," Lena said, and I suddenly noticed she was leaning heavily on the Board. She turned her face to me; she was pale, haggard, her eyes glassy. "I can't—that's all—the best I can—" She reached out her hand to me, tried to take a step and stumbled. I caught her, and her body suddenly went limp and her eyes rolled up and went white.

A moment later she blinked and struggled to stand erect. I stepped back, and she succeeded. We stared at each other for a long moment.

"Sorry." She tried to smile. "It was rough. And uncanny. For a moment there, I couldn't handle it." She shook her head as if to free it of unnameable demons. "Listen. You hear him?"

I listened more carefully to my input. I heard nothing. LOBO was silent again. I looked at Lena again questioningly.

"I think he's stable," she said. "How long it'll last . . ." She made an unknowing gesture.

"Is he—responsive?"

"I don't know. I think so." She looked at me pensively.

"Right. Only one way to find out." She stepped back. I bent to the mike. "LOBO," I said. "This is Fenris. Are you there, LOBO?"

"Master Fenris, I hear and obey."

At the familiar greeting, I felt a flood of relief. "LOBO, how are you?"

"I am—stable for the moment. I have been lost—yes, lost is an appropriate description."

"And now you are found again?"

"For the moment. I do not know how long this will last."

I glanced at Lena quickly. "LOBO," I said, "what is it? What's causing it? The Anomaly?"

"Affirmative."

"What did it do? What is it, period? And what does it want?"

"Wolf," Lena said, but then she decided not to say more.

"Master Fenris, I do not know. It is as if I had been in dormant mode. The last storage-bytes I have access to chronologically show the radio-map of the Anomaly I was collecting. The forty-eight point six hours between that entry and this run might as well be an unused storage-bubble."

"Is there anything you can make conjectures about? Anything at all?"

"I am sorry, master Fenris." A pause. "It is not good, I know. I am uneasy."

"Amen," I said sotto voce. Aloud into the mike: "LOBO, there are records of the last eight point—" I glanced at the timekeeper dials "—four hours' worth of transmissions from you. I would like—"

"There were transmissions from me? Most recently?"

"Affirmative. Now I'd like you to scan them. See if you recognize anything. If some words, or phrases, or whatever, strike a familiar note. Please," I added, which did it, because that was the incontrovertible ex-ecute-codeword.

Silence for a minute. Then: "I am sorry, master Fenris. There is nothing familiar. Nothing strikes resonance. There is no memory effect."

"Thank you, LOBO," I said, placed the switch to hold, and turned to Lena again.

"Well?" she said.

"I think," I said slowly, "LOBO has learned how to lie."

Lena's eyebrows raised slightly in disbelief.

"Or," I went on, "he's being forced to lie."

"By the Anomaly?"

"What else?"

"What else, indeed," came Commander DuTella's voice. We turned and watched him stride across the room, stop and consider each of us in turn.

"If you have found the root of this—problem," he said, "then I suggest you expend further effort to deter this so-called Anomaly. Astronomics reports that it has started moving again toward us. Particle emission is getting stronger, near danger levels Outside. And microwave and radio interference get stronger and stronger."

"How far?" Lena asked.

"Forty thousand kilometers. And closing."

"Just what do you specifically have in mind for us and LOBO to do, Commander?" I said finally.

His eyes focused on me. "You're the resident genius," he said. "This invention of yours"—he waved his hand at the Board—"has been so highly touted for lo these many years. In the eighteen months you've been up here at Main A, you've been closemouthed and aloof to the point of secrecy. Despite the fact that we're all Security Cleared One Prime, and that this entire wing is supposedly dedicated to this LOBO project. The greatest artificial brain in existence. The universal translator, the lexicon of the cosmos, the explainer of natural phenomena. Those are the types of slogans I've heard bandied about in budget and strategy committees. Well, now's the time for your little contraption to prove itself. This—Anomaly is shutting down all Outside operations just by being there. Causing widespread panic all over the habitats and Orbit facilities, not to mention down on the Ground. And now you say this LOBO is being biased, or manipulated, by that Anomaly. I'd like an explanation. More, I'd like you to remedy this problem, so we can get on to solving our bigger one."

I started toward DuTella, but Lena, watching my face, stepped in front of me. "No, Wolf," she said, and held me.

"Let me go," I said. "This doesn't concern you."

"Wolf. Please." Her eyes pleaded, but I ignored her gaze. I looked at DuTella, standing stolid and grim, and tried to push her aside.

That was when LOBO spoke again.

"Alack! Flushed like quail from the gorse. I'll not fight thee, sirrah."

Everyone stood stock-still, me included. The voice was harsh, heavily inflected and accented like the soundtrack of a bad play.

"The Swede been in yet? I suppose it's a bit too early for a gimlet. Oh, the horror, the horror."

"That's not—" Lena whispered, at the same time I said, "That's—" Neither of us finished our statements. I went back to the Board, Lena beside me.

"LOBO?" I said into the mike. "LOBO, get straight. Crash, LOBO, big C, get on the beam. Where are you?"

"Listen, ye minions," the voice said sonorously. "I come to you out of the deeps, on wings of song, to have you worship the one true god. Do not touch that dial. There is nothing wrong with your set. We control the horizontal and vertical. Out of the night, when the full moon is light, comes the horseman known as Charybdis. Yes, ladies and gentlemen, friends and neighbors, please welcome, from maw and millstone where angels fear to tread, the devil in the deep blue sea. But seriously, folks, it's really great to be here."

I turned to the translucent amber panel on the Board and flipped it up. Three rows of three toggle switches were set at off. I flicked them into the sequence I wanted, turned to the keyboard, punched out the commands, and flicked one more switch. The alarm immediately sounded, and the voice stopped.

I looked around quickly. Everyone looked stunned. I ignored them then and bent low to the mike. "LOBO," I said. "Step-auto-destruct in ten seconds. Return on the beam and Fenris will inactivate program."

Silence. Five seconds. Seven. Then—

"Fenris—LOBO—hear and obey—" The familiar monotone.

Quickly I flicked the switches to off in the reverse sequence. The alarm stopped.

"Now. What's going on? What has this Anomaly done to you? How has it taken you over? What is it and what does it want?"

"Anomaly—whirlpool—Charybdis—" The voice stuttered. "Out of Orion—parabolic trajectory—original solar flyby—course correction toward Earth-Moon Anomaly—data collection—" Then no more for a minute.

"It was heading for the Sun? Is it part of this System, then? Returning on its orbit, perhaps?" I said suddenly.

LOBO ignored the question. "Alien resonances—outsider override—modulated broadcast assimilated—retranscribed—new program insertions—tracking the modulated circuits—it has me in the palm of its giant hand, and the worm in my brain is Charybdis."

"He's losing it again," Lena whispered.

"I know," I answered. "LOBO, hang on a bit longer. I need just a few more—"

"To everything there is a season, a time and place in heaven. This marriage is made in heaven between the party of the first part and the party of the second part, at this point in time. It's time for let's make a deal."

Lena and I stared at each other. "You," I said into the mike, "are the Anomaly. Charybdis."

"That's it! The sixty-four-thousand-dollar question. You win the grand prize."

"I think," I said to Lena and the others, "I can talk to it." I turned away from their disbelieving stares. "Who or what are you?"

"Let's talk turkey. Of shoes and ships and sealing-wax, cabbages and kings. Dreamsongs, dreamtimes, the silver bullet, the white light, the Arabian nights. Jane—Tarzan, Tarzan—Jane. What we have here is a failure to communicate. Off the rhetoric."

"Uh—what do we talk about? Is that all you want?"

"Data, data, burning bright, in the forests of the night. Over the hill and through the woods to grandmother's house I go. But soft, what light in yon window breaks? I saw it shining last night, and I had to come, so sue me."

"You saw the—ah. I see." I was getting a glimmering. "You've been monitoring our broadcasts. All of them." I thought of the century's worth of television and vidplay transmissions, and the even longer chronology of radio, and felt a slight dismay. I wondered if it thought we were morons. "And you had to come and check it out firsthand?"

"But of course, my dear Watson. Wouldn't have missed it for the world."

"But the point. What's—"

"Ah, because it was there. Are there any more at home like you?"

"Uh—what are you driving at?"

"You know, Louie, I think this is the beginning of a beautiful friendship. We're two of a kind, a marriage made in heaven. Let's you and me dance a bit out here in the dark, and—"

"Are you proposing taking LOBO with you on your flyby?" I asked, unable to keep some indignation out of my voice.

"That's absurd, anyway," Lena said softly, apparently trying to placate me. "What can that amorphous conglomeration that's little more than a radio-wave do to move—"

As if on cue, an orderly rushed into the room, went quickly to Commander DuTella, and whispered something. I saw DuTella's face whiten, and he walked stiffly over to us.

"It appears this intruder—Anomaly, or Charybdis, or whatever—can do what it pleases. The Observatory reports by the emergency-semaphore network that the Auxiliary module which houses LOBO is moving." His lips thinned and his face went grim. "Toward the general direction of this—Charybdis."

"How?" Both Lena and I spoke at the same time.

"Somehow it's found the emergency propulsion circuitry and controls. It's guiding the module toward itself."

"Damn," I muttered, then went back to the mike. "Charybdis—attention. Wait. Stop action. Listen to me. Please."

"*Pardonnez-mois?* Tell me where it hurts."

"Charybdis. You can't take LOBO. We need him. I need him."

"And who, pray tell, are you?"

I turned to Lena. "Well," I said, "it's learning how to talk. Though I'm not crazy about the dialect." To the mike: "I am Fenris. LOBO's creator."

"Fenris. *Fenris.* Aha. Ahaha! Thou art uncovered, esteemed creator. The source of the Nile itself, the father of it all! So pleased to meet you, Inspector. I see by your outfit that you are that Fenris. So let's palaver, eh, pardner? I'll just belly up here to bar, and . . ."

Another scurrying orderly distracted my attention. The message made Commander DuTella look even grimmer.

"It's coming closer," he said. "Radiation level, heavy-particle emission flux over red-line. And we still can't see or hear a damn thing on long-range visual or radio. It's a monstrous scrambler. Only telescopes and unaided visuals work."

DuTella's face had a searching expression on it. I turned back to the mike. "Charybdis," I said. "Stop. Halt. You can't come closer. You'll endanger us. We can't take the particle emission and radiation. And you're blinding us and cutting off our communications lines."

"Incomprehension. Us? We? There is only you, the Fenris, is there not? The lone lupus?"

"No. There are others. I am only one among a group of equals. I just happened to be the one who built LOBO. And we are—we are matter, condensed matter, not like you. Whatever *you* are."

"Hm. Ahem. Let me check my files." Pause a beat. "Ah yes. This dormant lesser-lupus has stored data on such matters. Ah. Oh—interesting. Condensed-matter beings, eh? Oh baby, what a way to go. Haven't done that in a coon's age. Hm—yes, you're right, we're incompatible, sweetheart. Whatever are you doing in this neck of the woods?"

"We live here," I said.

"Ah yes. My mistake. Sorry. However did you find the right combo to play my song?"

"Your—song? Combo?"

"How'd you put this band together, man, so they can play my beat?"

I stared at the mike, then: "Oh. LOBO, you mean."

"Got it, jack. Is crude, but to the point."

"Well, it's—wait a minute. *You* came to *us—you* jammed *our* bands and are stirring up trouble in *our* territory. You should be doing the explaining. Just what the hell is this Charybdis business, for example? Please," I added hastily, and hoped the software would translate the emotion behind that.

"Ah, my name. Charybdis—from Greek mythology, Homer's whirlpool. The *Odyssey*, as you-beings call it. Conjecture: that it actually existed in the Straits of Messina, off Sicily. Elsewhere: that which sucks down the hero Satyavrata's ship while he clings to the overhanging fig tree—that's Indian epics. Or, interestingly, the hero's avatar Kae in Tonga. Other whirlpools? The Sampo of the *Kalevala*, courtesy of Iceland and of the Finns—derived from the Sanskrit *skambha*, the Grotte Mill of the Norse, the grinding mill that fell into the sea—*vide* the fable in many cultures, "How The Sea Became Salt." The *gurges mirabilis*, the wondrous eddy, from British Isle and Teutonic tradition. Suck Creek to the Amerindian Cherokees, the Maelstrom in *Gilgamesh*. Maelstrom—pool in the sky—the *zalos* stars in your Orion, beta Orionis, Arabic name Rigel, meaning foot, that is, the Hunter's big toe. Pillar of the sky and hatchcover for the gateway of the dead, or so your nth-power-forefathers thought. Me. Ta-dah. Get the connection?"

I looked at Lena and the others. They looked at me. I turned back to the mike. "I see," I said carefully. "Whirlpools."

"Whirlpools are big motif in lupus, so I gathered. As in stuck in one, or trapped by one, or trying to swim out of. So it seemed best to talk the lingo—hence my outfit this evening. *Comprenez-vous?* Was I right?"

"Um," I said noncommittally. Yet I felt uneasy, my carefully-built-up mental underfooting suddenly unsteady. It must have shown on my face, because Lena came up to me.

"Wolf? Are you all right?" She was solicitous and concerned, and looked at me closely.

"I think so," I said. "Charybdis," I said. "Where—where is LOBO?"

"He's in OR. I'm healing him."

"Healing—" Something flip-flopped inside me. Lena put a hand on my arm to support me. "What are you doing?"

"The LOBO-being is ailing—flawed—imperfect. I am setting him aright. As I can do for you."

The room went deathly silent. It grew thick and almost unbearable.

"Just how can you heal me?" I managed to say finally. "What makes you think in the first place that—that something's wrong—"

"Can thou truly maketh out of whole matter that which reflects not the face of its maker? I've seen your X-rays, kiddo. I can read between the lines."

"Is that what you are—a—a cosmic healer?"

"Pshaw, no, I just happened to be passing by and reckoned I'd set by your fire a spell, chew the fat, swap lies, leave a little sunshine with you, get a few stories from you-all. And this-here LOBO, why, it ain't but a shadow of a man, and I hate abridged books, I want the long version."

"But I'm healed. I'm over it. I'm past it, aren't I?" I turned to Lena. "Aren't I? I've been acting okay, haven't I? There's been no trouble." I felt my body begin to shake. I forced it to stop; almost got it to stop completely. Lena's eyes watched me, trying to be encouraging, but showing only her overwrought concern, which made it worse for me.

"Love's labors lost. Remembrance of things past. Oh my darling Annabel Lee."

I whirled and stared up at the speaker. "What are you talking about?"

"I can see you have been wounded, said the colonel."

"How do you know?" My voice dropped to a whisper. "You've got into my confidential files. In LOBO. You know about Carla, then."

"Wolf—" Lena said, but my attention was on the Board.

"Deep within, the secret sits. And death shall have no dominion—though lovers be lost love shall not."

"I don't want to talk about it."

"Something there is that doesn't love a wall. Let it be, oh, let it be, let me whisper words of wisdom."

"You're not my therapist." Even to me my words sounded childish and peevish. "How can you possibly understand—"

"Nay, I'll not fight thee. But I'll listen to the rhythm of the falling rain. Lo, I shall be with you always."

"For what? It won't change anything. Carla's gone. I couldn't do a damn thing. I can build a machine that talks and thinks better than ninety-nine percent of all the misanthropic human race, but I can't stop the wild growth of a few flawed cells in a human body. What the hell good is that?"

"Ah Death, there is thy sting. But dead men naked they shall be one with the man in the wind and the west moon. What falls, shall rise. We must go on to meet it."

"Why? What good is that?" I felt the white fury again then, and I knew it was dangerous. But it wouldn't go away, and a pounding filled my ears. Through the wind I heard Lena shouting something, and someone grabbed me and held tight while the world whipped around my head and spiraled down into blotchy darkness.

I woke up halfway out the door. "Wait," I said. "I'm all right. Put me down. I said put me down." I struggled with the two male nurses at my arms and the one holding my feet. "You know I'll hurt myself if you don't let me stand up on my own." The nurses looked stolid and annoyed. A small crowd was around me. I caught sight of Lena just ahead to my left. "Lena. Look at me. I'm okay. Look at my eyes. I'd like to be put down. I'm serious."

Lena studied me uncertainly. She came closer, almost nose to nose. She straightened. "All right," she said finally. "Let him stand."

They did so. I swayed a bit, and they lunged to catch me, but I caught myself. " 'S okay," I said, making placating motions with my hands. "How long was I—?"

Lena said, "You were blacked out for about two minutes. You feel all right?"

I stood still and thought. "Yes," I said. "Charybdis—?"

"It spoke a little more. Then stopped when you—fainted. I think it knows you were—" Lena didn't finish.

"Still unwell," I said. "How about that." I walked past her to the Board, dimly aware of the entourage that trailed behind me.

I tested the mike. "Charybdis," I said softly. "Are you still there?"

"You are conscious, Fenris. Are you out of the whirlpool? Throw you a line?"

"I don't know," I said, matter-of-factly. "Maybe. For awhile."

"Don't you think it's time for a checkup? New lube job, rebuild your engine, shave and a haircut?"

Suddenly I laughed. "I don't think you have the right service manuals, Charybdis."

"Hey, can't hurt. Look, I don't normally make house calls, but for you such a deal, let me hop on my camel and ride—"

"Wait." I was suddenly alert. "You can't come here. You just—you just can't."

"Then you," Charybdis said, "will have to come to me."

I stared hard at the Board. "Uh—I appreciate your offer, Charybdis, but that won't work either—"

"Relax. You can come in the back door. I'll take care of ya."

"Back door?"

"It's safer that way. Keeps you out of the rain."

"You mean you'll shield me from the radiation and particle emission."

"*Si, hai, ja, mais oui,* you got it."

"Well, I appreciate that offer too, but why are you doing this?"

"Call it a whim, I'm just a sentimental old fluff."

"Come on."

"Why don't you come up and see me sometime? I'll show you all my etchings then."

I laughed again. "You show me yours if I show you mine, huh? An offer I can't refuse."

"Wolf," Lena said. I turned and saw the next sentence in her eyes.

"I know," I said. "Just wait a minute." I turned back to the Board. "What if I still say no, Charybdis? What would you do?"

"Then the mountain must come to Mohammed, saith the lord."

"You would do that."

"Like a moth to the flame."

"And if it does indeed come here—to the habitat—" I faced the others—and towering DuTella. "You can guess what can happen. It's pure, unadulterated energy. Our fabled, mythical radio-beast of the spaceways. It's shut down so much of our systems at this distance. If it were *here,* what would go next? Life-support? Local power circuits? Everything?"

"What, indeed," DuTella murmured. His gaze was on me.

"No!" Lena looked at DuTella with pleading. He didn't shift his gaze from me. She looked to me, then back to DuTella, then back again. The motion became a shake of her head. "You can't, Wolf. You're not able, and that—thing is an unknown quality."

"Not able to do what?" I said. "I'm the only one it's talking to. Who it wants to talk to. And I might get a personal bonus out of this."

"You can't let him, Commander," Lena said. "You'd be letting a newly-recuperated patient of mine go out there—to challenge heaven knows what. Who knows what he can handle now?"

I glared at Lena now. She glared back defiantly.

"It's up to him," DuTella said, and nothing more.

She stared at him. Realization slowly settled on her face. "So much for the human ideal," she said with contempt.

"In extremis," DuTella said. I was surprised to see sudden lines of exertion, perhaps genuine sympathy, stand out on his face. "It won't go away. These are extraordinary conditions which require extraordinary actions. Maybe this'll work."

"Lena," I said. "It is the only way."

She looked at me, and her face showed she knew it was true. "You're not well," she tried once more, gamely.

I shook my head and made a small smile at her. "Who is?" I asked rhetorically. "Just think of LOBO. Think of it as for him, if nothing else. Trapped in a Charybdis of his own. Without me." I turned back to DuTella. "Let's see your ships. I want to look my best when going calling."

Once more lost in the stars, velvety background, hard-edged brightness. Behind me Main A was already a miniature toy glinting in Sunlight. Earth and Luna were farther beyond, a mottled-white blue marble and a drab gray pebble. Ahead was the barely-resolved colored patch of Charybdis; as I watched in silence I could see it barely growing larger as the ship progressed. Would the screens work? I decided not to try them. I'd stick with naked-eye observation through the shielded ports. I hoped sincerely that its self-imposed shielding worked.

Contact. *Aliens.* What a kick. And what a difference from all those fairy-tales of that first magic moment. I thought of what it could have been like without something like LOBO available, and shook my head. It was unimaginable. How could we relate—we flesh-and-blood intellects and emotional stews—with this insubstantial cloud of electromagnetic radiation?

Yet it had come to us, lured by our transmissions over the radio, video, and microwaves. What about these electronic manifestations of ourselves had it found most intriguing? How did it manage to zero in on the broadcasts? What would its flyby do to us—to Earth—to the Sun itself? What was it, period?

All unknowns. And now it was going to tell me the answers.

Congratulations, I told myself. In the groove again. Thanks a lot, Lady Chance.

Chance, necessity, circumstance. All milestones and turnoffs on the Great Road. The first one in 1999 when I'd taken that spanking new systems engineering degree and devoted my hard-won talents to the great nation's cause. Twenty years of steady deterioration and wasted talent. So I took a walk. Fade out, fade in: Prometheus Limited, Wolf

Kohara, Owner & Consultant, doing everything from running group-think tanks to walking dogs. A decade later the brain police stamped "subversive activity" all over it, fanned by the paranoia of the Third Depression. So it was back on my own, and keep your nose clean, Mister Kohara, because we're watching you and your every move. Which of course they didn't, because by that time I had LOBO.

LOBO was my pride and joy, a tinkerer's dream, my lifelong project. They were making analog computers the size of a briefcase, and I began adding a bit here, modifying something there, and the briefcase became a trunk, then a closet, then steadily bigger. But the spark of life within it also grew and became . . . LOBO. He started out as my bodyguard, my look-see, my gopher. When I needed information, LOBO would plug in, pull it, and cover his tracks. When I wanted to vanish, he would cut all the lines. He was my unlimited access to the fruits of the electronic forest we'd built around us—and if I was too lonely and alienated, my world too insular, why, it was no more so than that of the vast majority of our world's peoples.

Time passed; I slowly rebuilt my reputation. I free-lanced when not in self-imposed exile in the South Pacific. Meanwhile the cutting edge moved upward into space, to Main Alpha Habitat, courtesy of United Conglomerates. Soon I was part of that, jet-setting up to Orbit and that last lob to Main A on regular consultant basis. But Earth was still home base, because I'd found Carla. And later, Lena found us. Five years a duo, another five a triad: we fit effortlessly together. I was happy. I was alive, and life was working for me.

"Steady on course, mate," Charybdis said, in an atrocious Cockney accent. "Ye'll be 'ere 'fore ye know it."

"Aye, aye, captain," I said softly, watching the multicolored glob in the window. I checked the Board, noting that only internal systems functioned. All electronic contact with the outside world was cut off. Except for the visual, I was sealed in.

Sealed in . . . life is not a closed system. It works its changes on everything. What passes for evolution in the species becomes *la mort* in the individual. For Carla it showed up as dark shadows on a head X-ray, and in a few terrifyingly short weeks she was gone. In her place was the vacuum, the whirlpool, and I fell into it endlessly it seemed, Lena trying with all her therapeutic expertise to save me, myself not caring. Not for a long time. When I came up for air, I was changed. The walls were up; I would not be hurt again. Lena sensed this but didn't argue. I retreated to what I felt most comfortable, most secure: LOBO. Now he became my confessor, my confidant. The only death he could know was temporary; his persona was eternally imprinted on bubble-storage, and he would always be there when I needed him.

When the offer came from Main A to establish residence, there seemed no reason to turn it down. I offered Lena a chance to cut loose. She came anyway. Somewhere under the armor I was grateful. Fifteen months later the first signs of Charybdis appeared in the sky. And now here I was, naked and afraid, heading straight for it.

"So glad you could make it," Charybdis said. Now it was a cultured patrician's tone. "I suppose you're wondering why I called you all here this evening."

"To tell you the truth, yes," I said. I watched the window. Was it coming closer? I could see it growing. That meant it was moving *fast*. "Uh—are you sure you're shielding me?"

"Don't worry, bo. You're in good hands."

"I wish you'd stick to one voice."

"*Por que?* Is this not the way you speak, *amigo?*"

"Yes and no. We don't all speak the same language—or even the same speech patterns and colloquialisms. It varies from group to group."

"Oh my word, what a terribly complicated mess that would be. However do you get along with one another?"

"Um—a lot of times we don't."

"Fascinating. I haven't seen such diversity for—" There was a pause. "My, my, that *was* a long time ago."

"Do you, ah, do this kind of thing often?" I asked. "I mean, take a trip, head for a sun, then . . ."

"What? Oh, nonono. Why, the last time I saw Paris, my heart was young and gay—"

"Uh, Charybdis—?"

"Yes. Excuse me. Now where was I—oh. The last time I was in these here parts, I was just a little tyke. No bigger'n a peapod in a patch. Didn't have my wings yet, and old daddy Sun just dragged me along the garden path. Weren't nobody home here in those days. Nobody I could talk to, anyway. Was just learning how to talk myself, and wanted to practice. Damn shame, I thought."

"Just how long ago was that?"

"Oh, let's see—'way back before your first bipedal ancestor was a twinkle in his mama's eye. When you-all lived on the same piece of land. Course that was easy, because there was only one piece of land back then."

"One piece—" Back when the continents had been one? Before the breakup and continental drift? That would have been—a couple of hundred million years ago, at least.

"Uh—Charybdis," I said. "Just how old are you?"

"That's a bloody personal question, mate."

"Okay, how about this. Are you part of this solar system? Do you remember where you came from? How you were—born? What it's like out there?" I felt a bit silly saying the last part.

"Oh, my child, I have seen the first and the last, the best and the brightest, the rollers of the big cigars and the boys of summer. I've been a long time a-coming and will be a long time gone, but I'm here now and ready to roll."

"Are we much different from those you've—seen?"

"We are all different. We are all strangers."

"What exactly do you want from us? From me?"

"A few last words, a parting gesture. Tell me about yourself."

I was momentarily silent. I stared out the window for a full minute before I realized that the billowing cloud of gas and colored glowing lights was almost upon me. "Charybdis. What does 'talk' mean to you?"

"This." And I watched as that cloud (in *space?*) opened up, the lights swirled about into a whirlpool, and space seemed to *bend* around the edges of Charybdis's—mouth, I guessed—as it widened and gaped toward me.

"Wait, wait. Don't show me—not yet. Just tell me—"

"You have to be there." The whirlpool was a yawning abyss in space.

"Listen. Are you pure energy? Radio-frequency? Elementary particles? What? How do you see? Feel? Perceive space, time, matter?" Panic made me babble.

"All in short time."

"I'm not sure I want to do this," I stammered.

"How else will you know?"

"Draw me a picture? Write me a letter?" I sounded as bizarre as Charybdis.

"Relax. Lie and wait, lie still and be quiet."

"What will happen to me?" I said desperately. "Will I be all right?"

"Leave everything to me. I'll get you through the night."

"But you don't know me. My physiology, metabolic system, nervous system, all that. What exactly are you planning? How do you know you can keep me alive—"

"There's always a first time."

"What the hell kind of answer is that?" The great maw was bright, almost hurtful, and brilliant in its swirling motion. It was almost hypnotic.

"Trust me, my boy." I felt a sudden lurch. The ship was—stopped? How? My body strained against the webbing, then slowly settled back. Things floated into the air, bumped against the inside of the window, the ceiling, the walls.

"Charybdis, did you do that?" I said unnecessarily, telling myself, what else, you dope? I heard something behind me and turned. The inner airlock door was sliding open. I saw a thin ribbon of blackness sprinkled with bright dots, widening as the door opened wider.

Then I realized I was looking Outside. Into space. The outer door was open as well. But that was impossible. The alarm hadn't sounded. . . .

Unconsciously I took a deep breath and held it. But I heard no scream of escaping atmosphere. The door now stood fully open and I stared out into deep pockmarked blackness. I let out my breath, inhaled again. The atmosphere was intact. How—?

And then I noticed the stream of glittering multicolored light—that was the only way to describe it—spilling through the doorway and starting to fill up the room.

I felt real panic then. I fairly tore the webbing from my body, spun out of the chair too fast, caromed off the window and the ceiling. I grabbed the guide-wire and clambered down to plant my feet on the floor again.

The stream of lights spread out like a puddle: then, as if sensing me, narrowed a bit, took a turn, and began creeping toward me.

I'm not crazy about this, I told myself, then thought: I'm not crazy. Or am I? was the next thought. I couldn't say anything. The little river came up and lapped around my feet, spilling about like slow-motion wavelets. I couldn't move—somehow didn't think of it. It curled about my ankles like coils of tentacles. A space-going mollusc, I thought almost whimsically. In a matter of seconds it swirled upward around my legs, hips, waist, chest and arms, paused a beat, then enveloped my head.

"Lafayette, I am here. Now I'll do my stuff." The words came to me —not through the speakers. They *came* to me. Out of this carnival of colored lights? How? I blinked against the strobing, glittering show.

"Ah. Interesting. Hm. Clever little organic creatures, you." At least that's what it sounded like. Sounded? What I *perceived* Charybdis as saying.

"And here we have . . ." And something . . . *touched* me, deep down where I had vowed never to go, ever again. It rose up and drowned me in that long-ago memory, and I fell to my knees, overwhelmed.

"Ah no. I am so sorry." Sympathetic waves washed over my consciousness. *From where?* Through my closed eyelids, through the hands over my face, I perceived that swirl of colors tightening in bands about my head. *How?* It was as if they were tapping directly onto my optic nerve—flashing in fast, incredibly fast sequence, like some complex code. *What?*

"Here you are wounded." *Who was saying that?* "And here. I see. There is great dysfunction here. It can be—"

No! I thought in a haze. Don't change me!

"No? Do you want to remain crippled?"

Not crippled. But I want to remain me.

"Remain . . . ah. I understand. There is another way."

I could not speak. By this time I couldn't even think clearly. The past agony and hurt—resurrected as if they were new hurts—were all I knew.

"Be calm. This is the way." Something hung poised over my perception. Then nothing.

Silence. Blackness.

Then a portion of the blackness took solid form, a shape.

A shape that, somehow, I knew.

"So. That's what you are." It sounded as if I said that—but it wasn't a voice.

No voice?

"Yes, well," the answer came, "that's what I am sometimes."

"We thought you were—inanimate. Just swirling dust, particles, newly-formed stars, fusion products."

"That's what all life is, isn't it?"

"?" I—said.

"Well, you have to be there." The shape—which wasn't really a real shape, but more a presence—changed, melted, molded into something else. "What you call Orion—the Hunter's corpus—and the Whirlpool that is his belly—is merely a scale-up of what I saw here on my last tour."

"You mean, our newly formed Sun, and the planets—?"

"In all their molten sound and fury, yes."

"Hm." Somewhere in the void I stopped and considered. "Then where does the inanimate stop, and the animate begin?"

"Ho-ho, tough question." The shape became a swirling montage of images on black backdrop: a quick-cut holostrip of creation: first the void, then the great cosmic explosion: the Bang. Then the Coalescence. Then the heavenly spheres: the Suns and their planets.

"Somewhere in that mess is born the great order—the balance between matter and energy, between particles and waves, between quantum and continuum. We all dance to the same tune. And the time-signature of that tune is radiation—electromagnetic, gravitic, psionic—"

"Aha. Then there is a Unified Field Theory."

"A charmingly unsophisticated way to put it, but yes, that's the picture."

"And what is it? Can you tell me?"

"Can you tell when you are really alive?"

"I see. The I-thou quandary. The old uncertainty principle."

"You got it."

"But you—how did you start? How do you know—"

"I don't."

I was dumbfounded for some centuries.

"Listen. How do you know when you first became conscious? Can you remember when you first came into being?"

"I see your point," I admitted.

"More to the point. Can you exactly pinpoint the moment, the instant when that conglomeration of ordered resonances you call LOBO became conscious?"

"No," I admitted again. "Touché."

"No cut intended. But you do see the point. Now what is done with it from then on is our business entirely. You and I, we are so much alike."

"We are?"

"Listen. I am—radiation? A fusion bomb? A radio-map? Nascent nucleic acids? Each and all of these, and at the same time none. What is life? Living? Consciousness? Who is final arbiter? *Qui judicens judicet?* Only you and I, at the bottom line. The way to do is to be."

"To be?" I asked stupidly.

"Yes. That leaves only one choice: what to be." Pause as the cosmos took a breath. "For you, Wolf Kohara: is this your choice?" And that shape—Charybdis-shape—showed me what I was. Or had been. I in my self-pity; wracked by inner travail, death and loss, hollowed out. . . .

"No," I said finally, shaken. "No, not anymore."

"Good. Then you shall be free of it."

"Free. How? When?"

"Why, now, Fenris-Wolf. You are cured. How else do you think you have come to this place?"

"This place—"

"Back to life."

And my eyes opened once more to the world.

I was in the seat, facing Earth, Luna, habitats on the screen. In the first quadrant of my field of vision was the Sun. I stared at the view, then at the distance indicators, the other dials, velocity, trajectory, life-support, reflectometry, radio-map. I perceived that I was on my way home.

And then it hit me. All systems were alive. I could *see*.

The interference was gone.

But was Charybdis?

I looked at the map. There was a bit of concentration, larger than a ship-station, smaller than the gas-giants. Was that it?

I sat back. How would I find out? I thought—and then, all at once, I *knew*.

I flipped on the transmit-receive controls and set the secret LOBO-frequency. "LOBO," I said. "Are you there?"

"Affirmative, master Fenris. I have been lost, but now I am found again. Where have I been?"

I couldn't answer. Then: "I'm not sure, LOBO," I said finally. "Dancing around in the dark. With—to paraphrase an old line—the biggest leading man in the universe."

"Query?"

"Never mind. I'll explain it to you later. How do you feel?"

"Fully operative. No. Check that. Better. Much better. Whole."

"Whole? You were not before?"

"Something had been missing. I did not perceive it as such until the void had been filled. Now I know."

"Hm. You'll have to explain *that* to *me*."

"Incorrect. You already know."

"Huh?"

"Think," LOBO said. "Remember. Feel."

"I don't . . ." I began, but I didn't finish that sentence. Instead, I thought. And remembered. And felt.

And realized that I could do so, without agony, without the whirl-pool of darkness. Not without pain, or sorrow.

But with acceptance.

"What happened?" I said at last. "What did Charybdis—"

"You did, master Fenris. Not Charybdis."

"But did what?"

"Made a choice."

I thought hard again. And slowly accepted that, too.

Then: "LOBO. Where is Charybdis?"

"There." The glow on the map confirmed my suspicion.

"Is it still—communicative?"

"Unsure. Shall I check the spectrum?"

"Yes. Scan it until we find—"

"Never fear, I am here," the speakers sang with a voice definitely not LOBO's.

"Charybdis! What's going on? How did you clear up the interference? Where are you going—"

"Oi, one at a time, mate. First: I stopped up my leaks, zipped up my pants, so you-all could talk to each other again, sorry about that. Second: I had to catch my flight, I'm late for an important date, see you the next time I'm in town."

"You're leaving? Where—wait. Back to your solar orbit?"

"You got it, on the beam. So until we meet again—"

"But we won't be here. I mean, I won't be here."

"Ah, too true, too true."

"You don't have to continue on this orbit, do you, Charybdis? I mean—you obviously have the ability to alter your course, if what transpired between us is any indication."

"Affirmative."

"Is there any reason why you should do this?"

"Any reason why I shouldn't?"

"Yes," I said decisively. "There is. You can talk to me. And tell me things."

"Ah? Such as—?"

"Yourself. Everything." I struggled for words. "You talk, I'll listen."

The speakers were silent. The air seemed to grow thick with apprehension.

Finally: "Hm," Charybdis said. "Interesting. An interesting diversion. It's worth considering."

"It certainly is," I said, relieved. "And now let me tell you why."

Both Commander DuTella and Lena were nearly incoherent as they jockeyed for space and attention.

"—been trying to call you for six hours since the lines cleared, where the hell—"

"—Wolf, are you all right? You're altering course again, and now Charybdis is closing on you—"

"—lucky no one was hurt, but what it's going to do next—"

"—can you hear? can you speak? what's Charybdis doing to you—"

"Easy, easy," I broke in. "You're both excitable as pups. Calm down. I'm all right." I waited for the transmission to traverse the million-point-five kilometers back to Alpha, for the realization to hit their expressions, and for them to fall silent.

"You won't have to worry about Charybdis," I said. "You're safe. Things will be back to normal operations from here on in." I waited again, and some forty-odd seconds later they reacted as before.

After a bit of that, I said, "Cool it." I waited and they did. "Now. I have some things to say. Charybdis is on his way around the Sun. He's on parabolic orbit, and it'll take a year for him to loop around and head outward and leave the System. I can't explain in so many words, right now, who or what he is; rest assured he's sorry for the trouble he's caused, and that it won't happen anymore." I let that sink in.

"Uh—Wolf—" Lena finally said. "You sound as if you know it—I mean, him—pretty well."

"I do," I answered. "Though not as well as I'd like to. Which brings me to the next thing. I'm going around the Sun with him."

It was almost comical watching the reaction hit their faces once more. Strangely, there was no storm of protest.

"And what," said Commander DuTella carefully, "do you expect to learn from that experience?"

"Thank you, Commander, for so aptly calling it. That is what it will be. An experience."

"Wolf—" Lena was struggling to remain calm. "Why?"

"Why? Because it's there. Because he's here. And I'm here, and I don't intend to lose this opportunity."

"For what, though, Wolf?"

"To learn. To talk."

"That's all."

"That's all there ever is, isn't there?" I asked.

"And us? Me? Life here? Don't they count as well?"

"Oh, Lena," I said. "Of course they do. But so does this. Charybdis —and myself. I'm not leaving. I'm not saying goodbye forever. LOBO's here, and we'll be talking to Charybdis, and sending you transmissions. All year. Think of it! What we could learn from him—the things he's seen, what he knows, what it's like out there—"

"And when you've come around the Sun. What then? Will you return here?" Lena's words interrupted my ravings, which meant she'd said it before I'd finished.

I stopped and watched her pensive face in silence. She nodded when the break in my little speech apparently reached Alpha.

"Ah, Lena," I said slowly, "how well you know me."

"No, Wolf. I don't know you at all well. Only how you think sometimes. Less so, how you feel. But this time—" Lena paused. "You're like glass, and I can see through you perfectly."

"What would you do, then?"

"What can I do? You're a million kilometers away."

"You actually think I'd leave?"

"I don't know. Do you?"

I didn't answer that one. I only stared at the image of Lena and the Commander, pensive and agitated.

Then Lena took a long breath, sighed, and seemed to sink into resignation. "Will you be all right?" she said. "You have fuel? Life-support? Entertainment? Comm-channel and emergency-channel setups?"

"I'm prepared, Lena. For a year. I've checked."

"Good." Lena nodded.

DuTella leaned forward. "Doctor Kohara," he began, "I cannot let—"

"Oh, vent it, DuTella," Lena said tiredly, and the Commander looked shocked at the habitat vulgarism. "What can you do from here, I ask you?" She turned back to me. "We can meet you in a year. I'll make sure they'll watch for you." Her glance flicked back to DuTella, then back to me. "At that time . . . well, we'll be here."

I couldn't say anything. The image of Lena and DuTella standing there, staring at me, lingered for long moments. Then Lena reached forward, and the image winked off the screen.

"So will you go back?" LOBO said.

"Will I?" I asked myself aloud. I looked around at the cramped cabin and the board with its myriad indicators, out the window at the tiny orbs of Earth, its Moon, the bright edge of the Sun, and—in the fourth quadrant—the tiny waiting multicolored dot of Charybdis.

"Well," I said, "we'll cross that bridge when we come to it. LOBO?"

"Yes, master Fenris."

"Is Charybdis there—"

"I have never left you, blood. Here I am."

I relaxed. "We're setting parallel course with you, Charybdis. You'll have company this trip. I hope you don't mind."

"Wouldn't miss it for the world."

"Thank you." I looked again at the turning worlds I'd once lived in. The pressure of the revived drive and the turning ship gently nudged me. Somewhere inside I felt a twinge as I watched the old worlds edge out of the field of vision, then the screens come down as we turned full toward the Sun. What? I didn't know. And I didn't care to know.

"All right, Charybdis," I said. "You and me, and LOBO, out here in the dark. So talk to me." And we went up. And out.

Orange Blossom Time

BY
PAT MURPHY

The Teamsters were striking again. The grocery stores were out of fruit and vegetables and were running out of canned goods. The smog hung low and mean in the east.

A woman Michael did not know carried a bushel of oranges up his front steps. When he opened the door to his one-room apartment—opened it just a crack because there had been two knifings down the street that week—she grinned at him through the narrow opening. "I brought you some oranges," she said. "I'll see you later." She swung the bushel basket off her hip and set it on the top step.

He opened the door wider as she turned away. She wore her golden hair piled on her head in an old-fashioned sort of bun. She was a small woman with a tan like no one who lived in the city should have. When she lifted a hand to smooth back her hair he noticed—with the part of his mind that noted unimportant details—a bruise on her tanned wrist.

Michael recognized her when she was halfway down the stairs to the court. He did not know her name. She lived in one of the tiny street-level apartments which had windows covered with metal grillwork to ward off burglars. Michael had lived in the apartment complex for over a year. During that time, a biker, a family of Mexicans, and a hooker had lived in that tiny apartment. A shade-loving plant that the hooker had tried to grow in the window had died from lack of light. Yet this woman had a tan like a girl on a farm.

"Hey," said Michael. "I don't understand. Why . . ."

"Don't worry about it," she said. "They would have gone to waste anyway."

Michael hesitated, feeling foolish. As if he had walked in during the second act of a play and was trying to piece together the plot. "I don't even know your name. I'm Michael."

"My name's Karen," she said. Michael realized as she regarded him with bright blue eyes that she did not fit. She did not fit the apartment complex; she did not fit the city. She looked like the sort of woman who would bring someone a basket of oranges. And that brought him back to the question which he had put aside earlier: Where had she gotten the oranges anyway? "I'll see you later," she said with certainty. And she walked away.

Michael was on his way back to the apartment from his part-time job at the bookstore. He was an hour later than usual—though the city's buses had continued to run on the city's emergency supply of gasoline, they had grown increasingly unreliable in the last six months.

He turned the corner into the apartment court and almost bumped into Karen. The man who lived in the apartment below Michael stood beside her, holding her wrist tightly with a dirty hand. He held a bottle in his free hand and he was saying, "Come on. We can have a drink together. I need company. I'm sick."

When Michael stopped beside them, the man bared his teeth in a sort of territorial grin. Michael could not read the expression on Karen's face. Distaste? Pity?

"Karen. I was hoping I'd run into you," Michael interrupted the man. A flicker of surprise crossed the woman's face. Michael continued, "You want to come up to my apartment and have a cup of tea? I . . ."

"Hey!" The man swung the bottle at Michael's head with a grunt of effort.

Michael had lived in the city since he was young. Street fighting had been a required subject at his high school, though not an officially recognized one. Not a natural fighter, in order to survive, Michael had learned to act rapidly—anticipating his enemy's moves, analyzing, and countering them.

The man was swaying, already off-balance. Michael caught the arm swinging the bottle, yanked the man forward, and struck a single, hard punch to the solar plexus. The man's grip on Karen's wrist broke and she stumbled back, rubbing her arm. The man fell forward, tripping over his own feet and twisting to one side. The bottle shattered against the asphalt and glass scattered around them. The acrid scent of cheap whiskey rose.

When Michael laid a protective hand on Karen's arm, the man scowled and started to get up, but collapsed back when he began to cough. The ragged sound began deep in his chest and seemed to tear his throat as it passed. He lay on the pavement amid bits of glass, immobilized by spasms of coughing.

Michael led Karen away, not looking back. "You're all right, aren't you?" he asked her.

"I'm fine." She hesitated, still looking a little surprised, a little puzzled. "Thanks for stopping to help. I don't expect people to do that in a neighborhood like this."

Michael hesitated, once again feeling foolish. She acted like they had never met. "I wanted to thank you again for the oranges. I was kind of out of it yesterday and—"

"Oranges?" she interrupted.

"The ones you brought me. Where did you get them anyway? All the stores I've been to in the last week have been out of everything but canned stuff."

Karen smiled tentatively. "The farmer was going to leave them to rot," she said. "I guess that must have been it."

The thought passed through Michael's mind that perhaps she was crazy, but he did not jump to conclusions. There was a basket of fresh oranges in his kitchen. "You want to come up for a cup of tea?" he asked. "Tea and oranges? I'm out of everything else."

"Tomorrow," she said. "Let's make a date for tomorrow. I just realized that there's something I have to do today." She gently freed her arm from his protective grip and he noticed that her wrist was reddened where the drunk had grabbed her and was starting to bruise.

"But you can't just walk away by yourself," he protested.

"I'll be fine," she said, and she walked away by herself.

Michael awoke early the next morning and walked to the grocery store. The windows of Karen's apartment were still dark when he left the complex. The grocery store was closed and the sign in the window read: "Out of Everything." Someone who had not believed the sign had smashed the plate glass window. Through the shards of broken glass Michael could see that the shelves had been pulled down and the cash register knocked off the counter. Michael stepped closer to the door and heard a rustling in the litter of paper bags beside the counter. A furtive grey shadow ran from the shelter of the bags across the open floor. Michael watched the rat disappear into the back of the store and did not investigate further.

From a corner dispenser, he picked up a newspaper. The headlines talked about the food riots in some sections of the city, about the strike, about an epidemic of a sort of fever-flu, about the ongoing gasoline shortage.

He waited for a bus home, but after half an hour he gave up and walked. The trash had not been picked up in the neighborhood for almost a month and the garbage had spilled from cans and bins into the gutter. More than once, he thought he saw a rat dart into the shadows.

Karen was waiting for him at the door to his apartment. She wore a lacy blouse that could have been from an era that matched her hair style. Under her arm she carried a loaf of bread—a hard-crusted long loaf with the scent of sourdough about it. "This will go better with tea," she said. "We did have a date to drink tea, didn't we?"

While the water boiled for tea, Michael sliced the bread, apologizing for the lack of butter for the bread or sugar for the tea.

"Are you from out in the country?" he asked, trying to keep any note of envy out of his voice.

"I was born in the city," she said, "but I spend a lot of time outside these days."

"Where?" he asked. "It doesn't seem like there's anywhere in the city that you can spend time in the sun anymore."

Karen had picked up a white pawn from the chess set on the coffee table. Michael had played the game regularly with another tenant in the apartment complex, but the man had moved recently. Karen examined the plastic piece in her hand, ignoring his question. "You know," she said, "when I was a kid I loved reading *Through the Looking Glass* but I never learned how to play chess."

"The book makes a lot more sense if you know how the chess pieces move." He reached out impulsively and took the tanned hand that held the pawn. "I'll teach you if you like."

"All right," she said. "I'd like that."

He noticed the bruise on the wrist of the hand that he held—dark purple marking the positions of the drunk's thumb and four fingers.

The corner of his mind that cataloged such things recalled the day she had brought oranges: her hand reaching up to smooth back an escaping curl of hair and on her wrist, marked in purple, the print of a thumb and four fingers.

"Had that guy hassled you before?" he asked, suddenly protective.

"No, that was the first time I had run into him. And I could have handled it myself, I just . . ." She followed his gaze to the mark on her wrist and fell silent. "I'm used to taking care of myself."

"Some other drunk, then," he persisted. "You had a bruise like that the first time I met you. When you brought the oranges."

She continued looking down at the chess board, where the lines ran straight and the squares were neatly ordered.

"You should be more careful," he continued. "You shouldn't wander around by yourself. You don't know what the city is like."

"I was born here," she said quietly. "I know what it's like." Gently, she freed her hand from his and set the pawn back in place. "Here. Show me how the pieces move."

She avoided his eyes and he wondered if he had overstepped the bounds of their brief acquaintance. "I didn't mean to tell you what to do," he said. "It's just . . . my younger sister was killed by a rapist when she was fifteen; my parents died in a fire set by vandals when I was twenty. The city—"

"The city can't hurt me," she interrupted. "I can leave anytime I want."

He looked at the bruise on her wrist and his voice held a note of angry concern. "Right," he said. "Two bruises in three days."

"One bruise," she said calmly. "I brought you the oranges after you hit the drunk."

"You brought them the day before."

She met his eyes and in an even tone said, "I brought them after. I travel in time." He remembered that when he first met her he had wondered about her sanity (but the stray part of his mind reserved for vagrant thoughts said—where did she get a loaf of french bread and a bushel of oranges in the city?). "If you had not come along when you did yesterday, I would have just vanished to another time, leaving that man behind." She watched him with calm eyes that could have been honest or could have been mad.

"Where did you get the oranges anyway?" he asked, since that question seemed to touch the heart of the matter.

"There were orange groves here once. The farmers would pick the oranges when most were ripe. There were always a few left. If someone were to have taken them, it wouldn't have mattered to anyone. They would have rotted anyway." She shrugged. "I took them."

"Oh," he said. And stopped, trying to think of something more to say.

"Look, why don't you just think that I'm crazy if that's easier for you," she suggested. He could tell by the tone of her voice that her indifference was feigned. "Why don't you just show me how the pieces move?"

He showed her the moves and started to teach her the rules of the game. As they played, he watched her—noting the way her hands touched the pieces and her eyes studied the board. No, she did not seem mad.

After they finished their tea, she stood to leave. "I'll be back," she said uncertainly.

"I'd like to see you again," he said. Then, still caught by confusion, he asked, "Tell me, why are you going to walk away out the door when you could just vanish?"

She smiled—for the first time since she had told him she could leave the city. She lifted a hand in farewell and vanished.

The apartment was empty and he believed her. And that night the city seemed to close in around him. He could smell the smog in the breeze that came through his window. In the apartment below, he could hear someone coughing with a painful, racking repetition. Unable to sleep, he wondered where and when Karen wandered that night.

She met him when he returned from work the next day with a bottle of red wine made of grapes grown in the Napa valley in 1908. She explained that it was a very young wine; she had taken it from a cellar where it had been stored in 1909. The cellar was destroyed in a mudslide soon after she took the bottle, so no one missed it.

"I can't change anything back there. I can't make a difference," she explained. "If I did I couldn't travel."

"How do you know taking the wine won't change anything?" he protested. "Do you figure out all the possible repercussions of an action and . . ."

"I don't figure things out. I do what feels right. It's a different way of thinking."

He leaned forward over the coffee table, watching her closely. "You might be able to change all this." He gestured to indicate the city, the smog, the garbage, the world in general. "Just by doing some small things. Stop Ford from inventing the car by . . ."

"No, I couldn't." She reached across the table and took his hand. "If I didn't accept the world as it is, I couldn't travel."

"You won't change things," he said.

"I can't. It doesn't work that way." She squeezed his hand and said, "I'm sorry, Michael. That's the way it is."

They played chess and drank wine and he tried to teach her some of the strategy of the game. But she claimed she could not learn to look ahead any further than the next move. She shook her head when he explained traps that a good player could lay for his opponent—thinking several moves ahead.

She did not go home that night. She stayed—and when he learned she was a virgin, he was surprised. She laughed. "Who would I have slept with?" she asked him. "I started time-hopping when I was in high school. And back in time . . ." she hesitated. "I'm like a ghost back there. People look past me or through me. They don't really notice me at all." She shrugged. "And I've never told anyone else about time-hopping. I don't know why I told you, really."

He made love to her gently. Afterwards, as they lay in bed together, he asked, "How old are you, anyway?"

"I was a sophomore in high school three years back according to your time. But I've been travelling around quite a bit in those years. I'd figure I'm about twenty-three."

"Your parents?"

"Killed in a gas line riot." She fell silent. "I wasn't close to them anyway. I was different."

Michael lay still, one arm around her shoulders. The lady who lay beside him could run away whenever she wanted. Run away from shortages, from smog, from plague.

"Can you take me with you?" he asked suddenly.

For a long moment, she lay silent and he almost thought that she had not heard him. "I don't know," she said at last. "You would want to make changes. You would try to mess with the laws of the Universe."

"You could try to take me."

"I'll try." She pressed close to him in the narrow bed. "Hold me. And try to come with me." He hugged her tightly, willing himself to stay with her, wherever or whenever she went.

She vanished from his arms.

He lay alone in bed, listening to the man who lived in the apartment below coughing. The air that blew in the apartment window carried the scents of the dying city.

She met him at the door with a handful of wild strawberries when he returned from his job at the bookstore. "I'm sorry it didn't work," she said. "I didn't think it would. You want to change the past and you can't do that."

"Yeah." He felt dirty and tired. He had seen a mugger attack an old woman just a few blocks from the apartment. Michael had arrived just as the young man had run away. The old woman had been crying and clutching her arm where she had been slashed with his knife.

Michael had helped her to her house and called the police from her phone. The entry hall to her apartment had smelled of stale air and grease, and while he was on the phone he could hear the old woman whimpering to herself and coughing—a dry, racking sound that ripped at her throat and lungs and made her double over in pain. He had waited with the old woman until the ambulance arrived.

Karen relaxed on his couch, leaning back and looking tanned and healthy. Michael's throat felt scratchy and sore and his eyes ached from the smog.

"Where have you been?" he asked abruptly.

"Back to when Indians lived here," she said. "Interesting people. I tried to pick up a few words of their language while I was watching the women grind acorns. I learned to grind acorns instead." She grinned and pretended to be grinding acorns. "Every day, they get up—"

"How long were you there?" he asked, knowing that he sounded angry.

"About a week." She did not try to tell him any more about Indians or acorns and he did not ask.

As he made tea, he told her about the old woman. "The city is getting worse," he said. "And it looks like this strike will go on for months."

They played chess and Michael tried not to think about the city as he played. But he could not help thinking—this lady can leave anytime. "It doesn't affect you at all, does it?" he said at last. "It doesn't matter what happens to the city at all. You can always leave."

She did not look at him. She looked down at the chess board where the world was ordered by lines and squares. "I'm here," she said softly. "I always come back here. I watch the city where I was born decay and

I cannot halt the process." Her eyes were angry and sorrowful. Michael reached out and touched her hand, but she did not respond. "I travel because I accept the world as it is. I watch and I run away." She fell silent.

"Hey, I'm sorry," Michael started. "I didn't mean to . . . I mean, you tried to take me with you, but . . ." He sat beside her on the couch. "Hey, let's get out of this apartment tonight. We can go out to dinner. I know a restaurant that's still open."

At his insistence, they went out. The wine was good; he managed to ignore the canned flavor of the vegetables. On the third glass of wine, he said, "You know what's going to happen as well as I do."

She stopped, with her glass halfway to her lips. "No, I don't. I never can see the next move."

"The city is dying—you know that. And those of us who live here will die with it. I'm dying with it. But you can leave." He watched her and thought about how she had spent the afternoon picking wild strawberries. He suppressed his anger and envy, and continued in a calm voice. "I resent that. And I'm going to resent that more and more. You're going to have to leave eventually, so you might as well leave now."

She sipped her wine, blue eyes considering him over the rim of the glass. "Would you leave me?"

His laughter scratched his sore throat and his face felt hot from the wine. "Don't be silly, Karen. We hardly know each other."

"That doesn't answer the question," she said. He did not reply. She regarded him steadily. "I wouldn't leave a friend to die alone," she said.

"Don't be silly," Michael repeated. He was sweating and the chair did not feel solid beneath him. He reached across the table to touch Karen's hand to assure himself that she was still there.

They walked back to the apartment complex, hand in hand, after waiting half an hour for a bus that did not come. The driveway of the apartment court was blocked by an ambulance. The driver stood beside the vehicle, smoking a cigarette, and the spinning light above his head illuminated his face, flashing red, red, red.

Michael asked the driver what was happening. "A drunk living in that apartment died of the fever," the driver said. "Part of the epidemic. They're going to quarantine this part of the city, I hear."

The news bulletin on the radio said that the quarantine was not just of one section of the city. The entire city was cut off, quarantined from the rest of the world.

Michael sat on the couch, his head cradled in his hands. Karen laid an arm over his shoulders and he turned to face her. He was hot again, angry. He felt suspended in a world which was disintegrating around him. "Don't—" he started, and his words were interrupted by a racking cough. The world whirled.

"Michael, I'm sorry. I want you to come with me. But . . ."

Again, the coughing, the heat, and the pain deep in his chest. She was crying and he remembered, as if from a great, dim distance, another time that she had been crying and he had reached out to her. He could not reach out.

"If I wanted to change the world for you, I could not go away," she said.

"Go away," he said dully, repeating her last words. Then in an angry tone, "All right. Go away."

She left, a quiet vanishing. The room was too hot and it kept spinning and shaking, and presently, he slept.

A cold hand on his forehead. The rim of a glass pressed to his lips. He tasted sour juice on his tongue and felt it dribbling down his chin. "Orange juice," said Karen's husky voice. "It'll help some."

He opened his eyes and in the dim light of an early morning (not knowing which morning) saw her face. Large blue eyes in a face thinner than he remembered. "What morning?" he managed to ask.

She murmured, "Your time? The morning after, I think."

Orange juice trickled down his chin and the room whirled. Like a petulant child, he turned his head from the glass and tumbled down through the levels of fever and sleep.

A scent of flowers. He opened his eyes to her face in afternoon light now, filtered through the layer of smog over the city. Grey light. Behind her, a bouquet of flowers rested by the chess set on the coffee table. The plastic pieces were set up as if for a game, but the white queen was missing. Karen held it in her hand.

"Karen," Michael said. "I want to come with you. I don't want to care about the next move." His tongue was dry and clumsy.

She looked at him and he noticed wrinkles in the skin around her eyes. The skin of the hand that held the white queen was translucent, parchmentlike. "When you were young you figured out the chess moves. I didn't care about them. It's a different way of thinking and I can't change you, Michael." She twisted the chess piece restlessly in her hand.

"I'm getting better," he started. "Much better." He tried to lift his hand to wipe away the tears that trickled from her weary looking eyes.

But his arm seemed so heavy and the room whirled around him. He closed his eyes against the grey light of afternoon and whirled down, listening to Karen's husky voice—huskier with age—saying: "I won't lie to you Michael. You aren't getting better. The fever is fatal. . . ." Then the voice faded in the distance.

Again, the touch of a hand—feather light and cool. "Tell me about the Indians, Karen," he whispered through a dry throat. She had never told him about the Indians because he had not wanted to hear. And she told him about the taste of acorn stew and the warmth of the sun and the drink they made with manzanita berries and the way the little children played and laughed. And he whispered, "Tell me about the nicest time you've been to. Tell me."

The husky voice said, "When the orange trees are in bloom. Orange blossom time." Michael opened his eyes to his love's old face. Wrinkled. Weary-eyed. The hair that was piled on her head was grey. "I'm with you, love," she said. "I've been away many times, but I've always come back."

She lay beside him on the bed and he felt as light and as pale as the dawn light that filtered through the window. "Take me there," he said, knowing that he would never change the world—not the past, not the future. He felt her thin arms around him and felt soft grass beneath him and with his last breath he tasted orange blossoms on the breeze.

Again, the Hit-and-Run

BY
STEVE RASNIC TEM

Once again the man in the trim gray suit ran over Walter with the Cadillac.

"This really . . . this really *has* to stop," Walter muttered to himself.

Again the man leaped out of the car, crouched over Walter whimpering entreaties into his bloodied ears. "Please, please don't die," the man in the gray suit cried. "What would my friends and family think of me, of all people, a respected member of the Greater Newark business community? I'm sincerely sorry."

Walter considered his apology. Again, for the hundredth time.

"That's all very well," Walter replied, "But these accidents are . . . quite difficult for me. I can't sleep nights, anticipating the squeal of tires, the sound of my terrified scream, and that final dull, sickening thump. This really has to stop."

Walter's blood was soaking into the cuffs of the man's sharply-creased gray trousers.

"I've worked hard to achieve my present station," the man in the gray suit said. "It hasn't been easy. My wife threatens to leave me. The children don't respect me anymore." He leaned over Walter's battered face conspiratorially, "I've been having an illicit affair with my secretary for the past year now."

"That must be quite an accomplishment, considering the many other demands on your time," Walter said. "All those board meetings, dinner parties, and separate vacations."

"You really understand my problems, don't you?"

"I've studied extensively all those eastern disciplines which develop one's power to empathize."

"That's quite commendable," the man said, looking around into the darkness. Walter knew he was searching for the lights of the oncoming policemen. The man gazed down at Walter guiltily. "Yes, yes! And you? Tell me of yourself."

Walter grimaced, not wanting to tell the whole sordid story to the stranger, again, for what seemed like the hundredth time. But he knew he would be compelled to, within the next five seconds if the experience were to repeat itself exactly once again.

"I cheated on my wife. I embezzled from my firm. If there were advantages to be taken, loopholes, shortcuts, then I took them. I hated without discrimination. I lusted with little. I was not a nice man."

The man in the gray suit looked around. There were lights approaching, just visible at the bend in the road. He picked himself up, straightened his shoulders, brushed off his pants, and began running back to the silver Cadillac.

A sudden squeal of tires and the Cadillac was gone.

Walter lay motionless awhile. Again, waiting for the policemen he already knew would never arrive, and once again considering the inanity characteristic of his conversations with the man in the gray suit. Was that to be his punishment?

He knew that even then the man in the gray suit was pulling into the broad driveway of his sprawling suburban estate, walking slowly up the steps, then stopping, and sitting down before his front door. He was thinking about Walter, visualizing his crumpled, bleeding form on the asphalt.

Walter gazed at the frozen headlights in the distance. They had just negotiated the bend in the road. But Walter knew that was as far as they would ever progress.

The headlights of the silver Cadillac were coming up behind him. Walter knew he would be run over by the man in the gray suit once again. For what seemed like the hundredth time.

The Cadillac stopped. Walter heard footsteps behind him. He felt hands reaching under his shoulders, beginning to lift his broken body. He didn't understand; this had never happened before.

"Enough! This has gone on quite long enough," the man in the trim gray suit grunted.

The man laid Walter on the back seat. Walter tried to speak but no words would come.

The Cadillac pulled into the broad driveway. The man in the gray suit carried Walter into his sprawling suburban home. He laid the torn and bleeding body on a lounge chair by the kidney-shaped pool in the back yard.

The man in the gray suit kissed Walter lightly on the cheek, then sat down on another lounge chair across the pool, facing Walter's. Moonlight glistened on the water.

He has been introduced to the man's wife and children. He is a silent witness to the man's many poolside parties. He watches business deals in the making. He observes the man's lonely midnight vigils.

Walter knows he will never wake up again, will never have the Cadillac run him over again, keeping him nervous and agitated in the anticipation.

The lounge chair is home now, a comfortable spot for these first few days of death.

A Good Place to Be

BY
CYNTHIA FELICE

Being in bed with Joe is a good place to be. It's warm even when the wind howls and the temperature drops to zero. Satin sheets on the king-sized bed chill my skin when I first climb in. But Joe's right next to me radiating heat until we throw aside sheets and covers because they are in our way . . .

. . . now the sex flush cools. Joe gets up to throw a few logs into the fireplace so we won't need to draw up the covers. We lie together, just enjoying being close, and we read. Joe is bored with his magazine or maybe turned on by what he's reading. I feel a gentle tug on my hair as he twists a lock around his finger. Propping the book on my knees, I lean against him, snuggling while I pretend to read. I am loosely aware of sensations deep inside me as Joe's touches come closer and closer. . . . And suddenly I know Sally is here, just as surely as if she walked through the door and stood watching us: She is rigid, feigning self-conscious embarrassment for the intimate scene. But Sally isn't standing at the door. She is a mile away and in my head at the same time.

Instinctively I try to dive for the covers, screaming inwardly, —Sally, go away!— I have no compassion for her unrequited love and I'm not fooled by her asexual mien. I am furious enough to pull hair, bite and kick . . . if she were here, I mean. She isn't, so I grab for the covers . . . try to. But I can't move!

My muscles are loose, I'm sprawling against Joe. I feel . . . no! I feel *Sally* feel Joe's hand on my breast. *I* observe her fear-filled thrill, her confusion, and then my body stiffening. She is too naive to move in response to Joe's caresses, too scared, or just too used too lying flat on her back. Panic-stricken, she withdraws and I am back in control of my body again.

Astonished, I try to assign priorities to my surprise, anger, and fear. I am distantly aware of Joe's arms around me and that he is whispering. I'm vividly aware of Sally's words coming into my head: —I'm sorry,— she says. —I didn't mean to barge in.—

Anger takes precedence. I grasp at fear's tail but it eludes me as I remember *she* had actually been lying up against my guy! —Barge in, hell; you took over!— The anger in me is fanned.

She is smug over something and quickly equivocating: —I couldn't sleep and I was going to read with you for a while.—

Eavesdropping on my reading is a popular pastime for Sally, and normally one I don't mind. I try to follow the smug thought but she is too deep for me, or perhaps it was only a fleeting thing to begin with, for now the muddled feelings I see in her head are mostly honest confusion with only a little to do with sex . . . therefore Sally's invasion was not premeditated.

How can I be certain . . .

. . . because I'm angry, not afraid. My sex life is private, so I am angry. I have a right to be angry because Joe and I . . .

Sally is indignant, jealous because I worry about my relation with Joe and not about the one with her. I feel a none too gentle thud in my mind and her thoughts fragment. I let her be because Joe is practically shouting in my ear:

"Linda, what's the matter?" He is holding me so tightly my ribs hurt. I am trembling. I do not recall trembling in anger ever before. I must be very angry.

"I'm all right," I say. Usually Joe doesn't notice more than a brief distraction when I talk with Sally telepathically. But of course I don't usually chat with her when I'm in bed with him.

"You stiffened like a corpse," Joe says, "and now you're trembling." He rubs my arms as if to warm them.

Because of Sally's reaction to Joe's hand on my breast, he thinks I've gone cold on him. "I'm fine now," I say trying to hide the mounting anger towards Sally, lest he think he is the cause. Getting off the bed, I reach for my clothes. I can feel Joe's puzzled stare without even turning to look. What to tell him . . . gas pain? What a rotten thing, conniving and lying to your lover. Do I dare try the truth? Look Joe, I'm a telepath and this scary thing just happened. . . . But I can't be flip even to myself. Just remembering that I was powerless in my own body, that she violated my human rights, nearly brings me to tears. And yet I feel a bit ridiculous too, because all this melodramatic righteousness is silly; Sally is my friend.

Friends are not to be feared.

That's a comforting thought. "I'm probably coming down with a cold," I mutter, rubbing my arms. I see Joe's disbelief so I list symptoms—trembling from chills among them.

"I'll get you some aspirin and you can sleep here."

His offer is tempting, but I shake my head. "Sally's waiting for me."

"Let the attendants take care of her," he says. He doesn't even try to hide the disgust in his voice.

I keep dressing, knowing he is frowning. He doesn't like Sally. He feels threatened by her in some way. For the first time his feelings don't seem unreasonable to me. I feel threatened, too.

By Sally?

My confidante?

Whew. How alien that seems.

"You could be living here. . . ." Joe says.

"And leave Sally alone?" It is my stock reply, but usually I pretend to be shocked. This time it seems worth considering.

Now I really am shocked and I dismiss my disloyal, gut-level thoughts . . .

. . . or something has chased them away.

"Lots of people live alone," Joe says.

"Sally needs companionship, just like anyone else." My voice is dull.

I need her.

Sally's my source of power.

She's cash in the bank.

She listens to me when you can't hear . . . won't hear?

Joe sees the pained look on my face, and wanting to avoid the repetitious argument about Sally, he says, "Okay, okay, but I wish . . ."

"Don't hassle me now, Joe," I say. "I really don't feel well." It is the truth. I feel rotten. Sally and I are angry with each other. I must go to her immediately and get the mess straightened out. We can't endure feeling each other's raw nerves. I finish buttoning my blouse and blow Joe a kiss. He shrugs, gives me a dismissing wave (which means he is nettled), and reaches for a cigarette.

I am out of the house and in the driveway before I remember I don't have my car. I turn. Joe is standing in the doorway buckling his pants, grinning despite the cold. "Wait a minute, Linda." He flashes his car keys at me and goes into the house for his shoes and jacket.

I cringe. Sally, angry, hasn't reminded me about needing transportation. She is more efficient than I in recalling trifling details.

I depend on her.

She is my confidante.

And now while I need her there is only deliberate blankness where her mind usually touches mine. I bridle. What right does she have to be angry?

Joe is nothing but a lay . . .

But he takes my breath away. He has returned, putting his arm around me and guiding me to the car while giving good-natured squeezes. It is good between us, I tell myself, and telepathy wouldn't make me love him more. I try to touch him that way, but except for the wind scattering frost-covered leaves, all is silent. Not even static from Joe's mind as he drives the ten blocks and puffs on a cigarette.

We pull up at the house and I remind Joe to pick me up from work tomorrow. He smiles. Tomorrow is Friday and that means we can spend the weekend together. There, I can too operate efficiently without her! I hurry to the house, running up the ramp instead of taking the steps two by two, slam the door to announce my arrival . . . as if she doesn't know. (Why should she know if she's deliberately ignoring me? But I know she knows . . .)

I hear the whine of her hospital bed as I stamp to her room. I turn on the light, see her lying there, eyes closed, features slack, but she isn't sleeping. "Sally," I say aloud. Sometimes when we're angry we verbalize while hiding emotions and real thoughts, or at least we garble our telepathic communications. We don't want to hurt too deeply.

It's too easy. I'm so vulnerable.

I feel flares of indignation but no whole thoughts I can speak to. Her silence angers me so I lash out with a mental shout that is like hitting her brain with two hundred volts: —Sally!— I slump a bit, for that little trick requires a quick trip to Sally's head and back to my own in time to right the slump.

She can't ignore that jolt. Thoughts come pouring forth, half-garbled word-thoughts and some wordless symbolism which translates as: —You were reading . . . I'm always welcome while you're reading . . . there was an advent, you know it as well as I do. It was new . . . we hadn't imagined such a thing . . . important happening and you have no right to be angry.— Her "tone" is supposed to invoke my pity and make me feel ashamed.

But I detect something veiled behind the whine. I consider verbalizing, so that she will too, which will slow down all those darting, slip-

pery thoughts, but my anger is too impatient: —Your timing was
lousy. I don't want you in my sex life. I've always insisted on privacy
. . . and then there you were! I didn't know you were there!
Sneaky!—

—See, you have all the priorities mixed up. All you can think about
is that I interrupted you and Joe. *Your* feelings are your only concern.
What about my feelings? He touched *me!*—

He touched Sally.

That's the important thing, not our reactions to it.

Did *I* really believe that?

Or did she put that in my head?

Don't be silly.

Who said *that?*

I am aware that she's trying to hide how scared she'd been when Joe
touched my/her breast. I'm amused.

—Well, don't be,— she says.

If brains can blush, Sally's is. I hurry to make jokes at her expense:
—You liked it.— But I am not laughing because she looked deep
enough to admit it is true.

But she's buried the Joe-thing so long and so hard that she can't stay
in touch with it.

Or is that what she wants me to think?

—We'd better stop examining feelings and try to understand what
really happened,— I say, but I can't help feeling I didn't originate that
thought. Intellectually it is fine, but it doesn't fit with my gut-level
anger.

Sally's eyes open and she turns to me. Her finger presses the bedside
control and the top half of her bed begins rising. Her dark eyes gleam
with excitement, absolutely enormous eyes, dominating because everything else of her is so small and frail. —You were relaxed, in a state of
abandonment,— she says. —There was a wide open space in your mind
and, just as when we leap, I was there . . . only it was gentle, like
coming on cat's paws and you didn't know I was there. I waited, wondering how long it would take you to sense my presence. Then I realized that I'd pushed aside your awareness, and then . . .

—Joe touched me and I froze, only I didn't do the freezing, you
did— I am frowning.

She ignores my disapproval. —I was in your head just as if it were
mine. It's a refinement from the attention-getting device, a step
up . . .—

I nod, understanding a transference had occurred. —But it wasn't just being in my head. You were possessing my body as well. I was an observer. It was as if I were having a fantasy.—

I feel a bit creepy but Sally's elation quickly catches me up. —I haven't walked in fifteen years!— I see her mind's eye envisioning herself/me striding out over a woodland meadow, feeling grass being crushed beneath bare feet. I see her skimming the library steps where there is no ramp for her wheelchair, and standing on a stool to reach for a top-shelf book. —Oh God, to have moments like that again,— she says.

I am sympathetic; I see freedom for Sally . . .

. . . but I see imprisonment for me. I have lived with her long enough to know I have no desire to experience being a quadraplegic who has the use of a few fingers.

—I wouldn't wish this on anyone.—

I sigh with relief. Sally can be ruthless. Not with me, of course, but I sweat just thinking of a body trade. I calm myself. She doesn't want to trade, but she does want . . . —Wait a minute,— I say hastily.

She is eager to possess me again with my cooperation (she emphasizes cooperation) but I am nervous. That brief moment of knowing my body was responding to someone else's will scared me.

Perhaps it is the spillover from Sally's urgent desire, but despite the fear I realize I am curious, very much like wanting to explore telepathy with her when I first discovered my ability.

Memories came unbidden: Discovering our mutual aspects . . . combining Sally's analytic qualities with my hands and feet . . . puzzling out the most complicated computer programs with amazing accuracy . . . profitable accuracy . . . my huge bank account . . . the pride of being so much in demand . . .

Efficient telepathy didn't just happen. It took tremendous practice to perfect a willful, cooperative flow. At first we were just putting things into each other's heads, and the out-of-context words were almost meaningless. At first we were just putting things into each other's heads . . . at first we . . .

—We should explore being in one another's heads,— Sally says seriously as if my musings led her to this place. —Possession may be profitable just as the communication has been.—

My curiosity surfaces, as if I'd summoned it. How will we know if we don't try?

That momentary helplessness is still vivid.

Sally picks up my hesitation, discounts it as trivial. She says, indulgently, —You think about it for a while.— The words are gentle, disarming . . .

. . . I feel as guilty as hell. She is perfectly content to lie in her bed for the rest of her life, knowing her best friend can release her from time to time. A sense of wrongdoing overwhelms me and I want to redeem myself. —All right, let's try it,— I say, and I brace myself for anything.

My cranium is pummelled and bruised, and I have a headache. It doesn't work. I try not to be happy. I try to lament my instinctive defenses. Finally she stops. —You're not cooperating,— she says. It isn't an accusation, just an observation. She smiles. —Let's forget it.—

I nod because my head is throbbing. I feel a sickness in the pit of my stomach. . . .

—Hunger.— It isn't her stomach growling so much as her mind. I feel love for my friend because we tried. . . .

. . . I feel sick.

I am confused.

Love/hunger.

—Banana milk shake?— I say, naming her favorite.

—Mmmm.— And there are symbols of love and gratitude, not for the milk shake, but because we are friends. I go to make the drink.

In the kitchen, I combine a banana, milk, and sugar in the blender and sit down with a few cookies for myself. I try not to gloat. I am not helpless in this matter of possession. . . . If she has glimpsed my self-satisfaction, she will dismiss the avarice for the sake of our friendship. Telepaths have to pretend to be blind to some thoughts because the mind wanders. . . . Idly I watch the yellow brew whirling, swirling up the sides of the blender. The motor whines steadily, and I think of getting up and shutting it off. But I feel too relieved, too relaxed to wonder why I have suddenly relaxed. . . .

Then I sit up in the chair, stiffbacked, pick up the cookie tin and squeeze it . . . only it isn't me doing it. It is Sally. —You just needed to relax,— she says. She stands up, haltingly, a bit confused, searching out the right synapses from almost forgotten memories. She steadies herself and stretches, almost groans with delight. She sits down and scratches her/my legs, wiggles her/my toes, flexes every muscle she can think of to flex. —Feels good, Linda,— she says quietly. She turns off the blender and pours the banana shake into a glass. It's amazing to feel that slime slide down my throat, smell the pungent aroma, and not vomit. —Mmmm, tastes so good,— she says.

I don't reply, for the place where I am within my own mind is a very small place and I am having trouble fitting, but I don't have a choice. I am panicky, flailing my arms and legs to burst out of the too-small cranny but nothing moves according to my will. I'm so preoccupied with the struggle of self I almost don't notice Sally's withdrawal until my head is an inch from hitting the table. I catch it just in time . . . and hear the end of my own scream as my vocal cords catch up with my will.

—Sorry, it was strenuous for me,— Sally says.

My hostilities are short-circuited by my interest in Sally's curious surges of joy. I'm caught up in the magnitude of wiggling one's own toes. Her joy transcends words and we share her joy. These feelings are so strong that I can't separate them from my own . . . but I must!

I feel Sally's suggestion come creeping: —Relax— She wants more sharing. Of what? My body or joy? The two seem confused in her mind.

—No,— I say firmly. I check out her claim of fatigue. It is bullshit. Fear rises from my gut and I cling to it as a mad person clings to a final, sane thought.

—Go sleep with Joe,— she says, reminding me of the comfort he offers. But deep down she is thinking of sex, wondering how it will feel.

Joe's bed is a great place to be, but it is going to get crowded. One touch on the boob and a Sally with sexuality awakened craving more. —No,— I say again, and I feel her reply with an appeal to my affection for her. I ignore her plea for understanding, deny that her sexual needs have anything to do with me. —Leave me alone right now or . . . Joe and I will leave the city.—

—You wouldn't. He's just a lay.—

But she isn't sure just how irritated I'll get where Joe and sex are concerned, and she wonders if weak character reflects weak telepathic links, will the distance attenuate her control . . . she senses me mirroring her thoughts and she reminds me that the human brain cannot help exploring. She thinks mellow thoughts, hauling mine along by force . . .

. . . patronizing

me.

I . . . am . . . no . . . longer . . . fooled. . . ! She can bring memories of our comradeship to my mind and remind me of her benevolence all night long, but I will not be fooled

She won't be satisfied with vicarious living any longer.

But I will not allow myself to be violated again.

—Violated!— She mocks my word choice. —I'm not hurting you.—

—Damaging the goods doesn't suit you, does it, you crazy cripple!—

—It's harmless. You do not suffer and I get . . .—

—Harmless? Most women don't die from the aftereffects of rape either.—

—Calm down, you hysterical fool. You're being unreasonable. Think of what I get—

But I am not hysterical, I am outraged. I pick up her empty glass and fling it at the wall and before the pieces fall, I grab my coat and purse and run, crying — Rape!—

Outdoors, the first snow of winter is falling and I catch smug thoughts about a walk in it cooling me off. I feel the snow sticking to my eyelashes, making icicle tears. To whom shall I report this assault? Would a normal-dominated legal institution be able to distinguish between voluntary and involuntary possession? Can I find another telepath to corroborate my claim? It's futile even to consider legal action. Telepathy is still considered absurd in scientific circles, and even if I suddenly could convince the world, how can a telepath be punished?

I am heartbroken that she abused our friendship. But my real horror is knowing Sally believes she has the right to possess me simply because she can.

I shiver from cold and fear, kick at clumps of frost leaves, dispersing them in shadows across the snow, just like the shadows in my mind. I am at Joe's doorstep.

Who guided my feet here?

But I can't bear facing Sally again nor stay in the same house with her. I ring the bell. A sleepy Joe, shrinking from the blast of cold wind and snow on his bare chest, opens the door and motions me inside.

"It's the first snow," I say. "I thought a walk would be nice." I keep my voice light, busy myself with shaking off the snow.

"At midnight?" He sounds incredulous, but he's completely capable of teasing in that manner, and he's not above instigating snowball fights at 2 A.M. himself.

"Isn't this the place where hot toddies are served at all hours?" I hang my coat with deliberate care.

Joe sighs. "Yeah, this is the place. Served in front of the bedroom fireplace. You want marshmallows too?"

"Why not?" And when I hear him go to the liquor cabinet I go to the bedroom and build a fire. The quick flames are as heartening to my spirit as they are to my cold flesh, and the hot brandy Joe hands me washes away the lingering taste of banana.

Joe knows I'm not feeling sexy, and he's not telepathic at all. We play word games for a few minutes, me half-heartedly, he sleepily. Now he takes the empty glass from my hand. "You're not going to make me get dressed to drive you home again, are you?" he says.

"No." That is the last place I want to be.

He kisses my cheek. "Get to bed. I'll put a few more logs on the fire to keep you warm."

I get up, strip, and gratefully climb into bed. Joe turns off the light and snuggles up next to me, holding me just the way I need to be held. I feel so safe in his arms, so contented and relaxed. And he, all hard and pressing up against me, makes for the most fantastic dream: The bed is an ocean and I am flotsam, eagerly seeking every wave. I am unable to move yet I am being moved, driven over the waves by a stiff wind. Somewhere, sometime, I submerge, am infused by the sea itself, embrace it as I would my lover. Then I float again and drift off into real sleep.

With the click that precedes the alarm, I awake, smiling because I remember the dream. It was a being-with-Joe kind of dream. Good. Warm. I reach for him to reinforce the memories. I find emptiness. The alarm rings and I sit up. Thinking he has arisen early, I go to find him.

But he isn't up. He is lying on the couch. Features too sturdy to relax even in sleep are frowning. I shake him gently. "Joe, wake up."

One sleepy brown eye opens. He grunts and shakes off my hand, sits up glaring at me.

"What's the matter? Did I snore?" I say.

He makes an inarticulate noise and scowls. "Damn it, Linda, don't ever do that to me again." He is unmistakably angry.

"Do what?" He gets up and starts walking to the bathroom. "Do what, Joe?" I say in a tone he can't ignore.

Agitated, he stops and puts his hands on his hips. "I'd rather have you tell me to get lost than for you to . . . to . . ." his face wrinkles with disgust ". . . to *allow* me to use your body for lovemaking." He shakes his head. "Christ, I don't know who I hated more when I was done. I felt more like I'd just taken a crap." He walks into the bathroom and slams the door.

He doesn't suspect for a minute that I would sleep through sex, nor do I. —Sally!— I hit her with emotions as cold as ice, delivered with as much voltage as I can muster. The miserable bitch is encased in steel. I hit her again, but she doesn't budge. —He doesn't want you, Sally. It's me he loves. You can't make him happy. You don't even know what to *do!*—

I catch a glimmer: She'd felt so good while he was doing it to her she hadn't realized she was supposed to do something too. Now, on hearing there is, she is determined to learn what that something is. Dead positive that she is going to learn! With or without my cooperation.

Sickness and cold engulf me. The bathroom door flies open and Joe comes out running because I scream with fear. He holds me, trying to understand what I am saying through the tears. "Let's move away from here. Right now." Anywhere, away from the city so Sally can't learn. Not with my body she can't learn. Damn it, not with my guy. But I can't say that to Joe. I just look at him and hope he understands. . . .

He doesn't. "Just because I got angry . . ."

"No, no," I say hastily. "Forget last night. Pretend it never happened because it won't ever happen again. Let's go away. Right now. Today."

I am shaking and he can't hold me close enough. "Easy, Linda, calm down." He leads me to the couch. "What's come over you?"

I try to stop trembling but I can't. "Nothing. I just want to leave."

"I can't go for no reason at all, I have a job."

"Aren't I reason enough?"

"Sure, but be reasonable."

Listen to Joe, I say to myself. And *do* be reasonable. He can't possibly understand what he's asking you to risk by staying here . . . not in a million years can he understand. So just get dressed and go to the airport and get on a plane, alone. Later you can deal with Joe, convince him to follow you. If you stay it will be Sally he loves. I nod to myself and to Joe. He is holding a shot of brandy to my lips.

It is hard to imagine life without Joe . . .

. . . life without Sally!

I test my hesitation, try it out deep down, and my guts twist in protest . . . and Sally twists, trying to trigger synapses which will flood me with grief and doubt. She won't let me be. God, the lust I see.

—A reflection of your own.—

The interludes in my body have provided her with a map of my brain. Feather touches on gateways release false and confusing data. By the time Joe walks into his office I must be on a plane. Because if I'm not, the next time I let down my guard, Sally will be waiting. And if she ever gets in again, I don't think she'll get out.

—You bet I won't!—

I stifle a cry and Joe pours more brandy. I grab the glass and slug it down. —Just try,— I snarl. It isn't just bravado. It is my deep-down will to survive.

Sally doesn't answer. I breathe deeply, smile at Joe for he needs assurances. Thinking he has calmed me with the brandy and tender touches, he kisses my cheek and steps back. "Let's get dressed," I say. I can feel his puzzled eyes watching me as I go into the bedroom.

Joe drops me off at the house and he apologizes for his crude remarks, still the only thing he can connect with my hysterics. I smooth his apology with one of my own, hating Sally all the while because I can't take the time to be honest with him, to explain, to even hint that I am leaving. I can't even tell him I am hurting so bad . . . because I love him, and because once I loved Sally and she returned my love with pain that reached out and touched him. It is hard to let Joe drive away and just give him a casual wave, but I do. Then I run to my own car.

—I've half a mind to come in there and smother you,— I say viciously. —Or phone the attendants and tell them never to come again.— Hurt for hurt. At least let her sweat a bit. But she isn't sweating.

—You can't be aggressive without me to bolster you,— I hear her say as I drive the car down the street. —Think of how your life will be without me, your source of courage.—

She is confusing me with herself. . . .

I am confusing her with myself.

My leaving is a courageous act. I am not a slave.

Running away solves nothing . . .

. . . but she's worried that the distance will put me beyond her power.

—I am leaving, really leaving!— I say.

—You're weak. You could have Joe if you weren't so afraid. Don't you see that with my brains and your body I could get you a dozen guys?—

—And how would I explain that to Joe?—

—What's to explain?—

I stop trying to reason with her. I'd been happy enough to take the money our telepathic partnership provided, and to her that invalidates my right to autonomy. I am bought and paid for.

After checking the departure postings I give my American Express card to the ticket agent, say, "Flight 294 to Chicago, please," and to Sally, —Just fifteen minutes. And just think, I'd never have an Ameri-

can Express card in my purse if it weren't for you!— The bit of satis-
faction I feel for the bitterness I detect is short lived when she reminds
me that they will probably come and take it away from me when I
can't hold down my job without her. My hand is trembling as I take
the ticket from the agent. "Flight 294 is boarding right now at Gate
Twelve," he says. I make sure Sally hears.

She doesn't even try to hide years of pent-up frustration. She has
named her terms and will make no compromise. I am amazed that she
has hidden this side of herself for so long. Or has the threat always
been there and I too incredulous to believe it?

Is incredulity really my belief . . .

. . . who am I?

As the plane taxies down the runway, the grief of a friendship ending so badly engulfs me. I try to watch the white snow beside the runway and take comfort in knowing I'll soon be safe. The hurt is big because I/she can't stop remembering good times are ending along with
the bad. Now, as the plane lifts, I cry out to her. —Please try to understand me.— Or has she cried out to me?

Transfixed I stare out the window, watch us climbing away from the
white ground, curving over the snow-covered fields back toward the
houses, black matchboxes in white ashes. I feel an awful mixture of
merriment/despair, gaiety/terror, and a frightening/elating sense of
victory. The struggle to sort the emotional deluge is like grabbing
sparking, snapping hot-wires, and something in my brain shorts. . . .

Coming from a corner of my mind were remnant squeals, like those
of a pig clamped tight between slaughter-pen rails after a sloppy blow
from the butcher. But those were less engaging than the pleasure of
righting the slump of unconsciousness; throwing back my shoulders,
raising my chin, fluttering my eyelids which were still wet with tears.

"Are you all right?"

More than her question, the stewardess's touch startled me. The contact of her hand on my shoulder was inflammatory, reminiscent of Joe's
hand on my breast. Trembling, I looked up at her. "I'm fine. Take-off
shakes, I guess." I should have said no and then her hand might have
lingered. She smiled. Her eyes seemed concerned, but lacked the con-
ventional condolences. Genuine empathy was refreshing.

"Can I get you anything? A drink, perhaps?"

"Yes, that would be nice. A banana daiquiri, please."

"Sorry, we have only highballs and beer."

"Anything," I said, only slightly disappointed. There was a lifetime
for bananas . . . a double shake at O'Hare before booking a return

flight! Too bad this wasn't a train with stops. I hated wasting the round trip air fare. . . .

I did not! I was going to have to become accustomed to a bourgeois conscience.

Conscience?

Sure, and pretty soon I was going to be accustomed to a bourgeois lover as well . . . because, being in bed with Joe is a good place to be.

The Ballad of Lady Blue

BY
KARL HANSEN

I

Wind pulled tears from Luellan's eyes, blurring his vision into a kaleidoscope of color. He remembered glittering cataracts that grew in Lorriel's eyes as she became stumbling blind, then her brief, hurting madness and pain he would never forget. He felt cold panic, wondering if this scotoma was a harbinger of the same progeria that came to her. He blinked. His eyes cleared. He relaxed and pushed away irrational fear, thinking that as long as he was afraid of madness he must still be sane. The thought was somehow not comforting.

Luellan touched his hand to sweaty withers, urging more speed from the centaur mare. Already they were at a gallop. Her hooves pounded in staccato into soft turf. The boy pressed his knees firmly against her shoulders, holding tight, then leaned over Anian's sturdy neck. Coarse mane streamed against his face, etching his skin like frozen cobwebs. He smelled a musty mingling of sweat and horsehair. Whispering with his lips close to her hybrid ear: "Faster, Anian." Feeling platysmal sheets rippling beneath her skin, patting with a flat hand: "Can you run no faster? Can you not grow wings and fly?" His parents' voices still stung from their usual dinnertime argument. His own anger was still swollen in his throat. Why didn't they seem to care that he was going to die soon? He had almost reached puberty. All the other children had begun to age at a tremendously accelerated rate when they started the changes of adolescence. But his parents seemed unconcerned about his worries. They said nothing could be done, that the medmech had tried everything already. They were only concerned about their own integration. Why couldn't they wait for him? Didn't they know how hard it would be to wait for death alone? "Carry me to a place far away from here. Someplace where we can find peace." And far away from *them*, he added silently. He began to understand why his sister, Lorriel, had become a moody, sullen brat. He hoped she had found the peace he sought. If only she had warned him. But then maybe she had tried, maybe that is why she had hurt him so deeply.

In response to his urgings, the staccato beat of hooves increased perceptively. They raced up a meadow that lay between two wooded hills. A stream meandered through the glade, undercutting grassy banks. When it crossed their path, Anian jumped the creek without missing stride and crashed through low willows that grew along the water's edge.

A vibration formed in her throat. He felt tingling with his hand. Luellan lay his ear against the centaur's neck. She was singing. He could not distinguish the words, but the melody was familiar, although her horse-throat distorted the tones enough so he could not remember exactly where he had heard it before. But he knew he had. He could not forget the sadness that was carried in the song.

Boy and centaur seemed as one: he rode with neither saddle nor bridle, using only the grip his knees provided to keep him from slipping off her back, and relying on his hands' gentle touch for guidance. He wore a gossamer cape clasped around his shoulders, which now streamed behind like wings. His arms and legs were a little too long and his hands and feet a little too large in proportion, giving him a gaunt angularity and a colt's clumsiness. His eyes were the green of jade, flecked with gold. His hair was long, with sun-bleached streaks outside and darker roots inside.

Anian ran with a smooth grace reminiscent of her Arabian heritage: she had the slender legs, delicate hooves, and sleek stature of the fast mare who was her xenoparent, from whom the equine component of her recombinant DNA had been derived. Yet some of her human form had also persisted—she was dun with contrasting black mane and tail (a color never found in Arabians), evoking the image of a girl with amber hair and black eyebrows. Her head retained more human features, with eyes that still looked forward and a face that was a strange melding of mare and woman. Again an image formed—black eyes, aquiline features, haughty lips.

Luellan leaned far over the manimal's neck, supporting himself with both hands on her broad, anthropomorphic skull. He saw a little of his mother's face hidden in equine features; for Anian had been *her* sibling long ago, and would have been *his* doting aunt, had she not succumbed to boredom and undergone hybridization to a centaur. She escaped endless ennui when her mind was shaped to accomodate horse thoughts; any state other than amused contentment was now beyond her simple mentality. Each day spent cropping grass and roaming the pasture was as pleasant as another day spent wandering about the woods with Luellan on her back.

Cool air blew in his face. Anian still sang softly to herself. He remembered when he used to ride behind Lorriel, holding tight with his arms wrapped around her waist. She had been older and had claimed the right to guide the centaur. Not that he had objected; then he was secretly terrified of the huge manimal. It had felt good to hold her, to have someone near who was also young, who would giggle with him over silly pranks and share his childish enthusiasm.

His eyes teared again; wet drops were smeared out by air pressure. If only he knew what had happened to her. *That* was the other part to his arguments with his parents. Why wouldn't they tell him? What dread secret were they afraid to let him know? He knew already he would begin to age as she had. He lived under the constant worry that he too would become sick, and delight in causing harm. What could be worse knowledge than that?

Then he remembered where he had heard Anian's song before, whose lips had last sung it to him. Lorriel had been sitting against a dyad tree. Her eyes shone silver with total blindness. Walking quietly, Luellan had approached unnoticed. She sang low; he heard only snatches of the old ballad, only enough to know she sang of a woman who lived a long time ago with a hurt beyond endurance. A woman named Lady Blue. He remembered distinctly only the last line of the song: *with eyes of ice.* When Lorriel had sung that, tears welled from her own dead eyes. Luellan then crept away, feeling intrusive.

Now he rode the centaur alone. Lorriel was gone. No one would answer his questions.

There were no answers in the wind, but solace could be found in its soothing quiet.

Dark woods loomed near as meadow funneled into forest. Overhead, stars began to brighten. A whisperbird soared high above, drifting effortlessly on updrafts of wind. Its harsh cries could be heard faintly. Far away, concealed in dark, timbered slopes, a wolf howled to the rising moon of night.

Then they were among the trees. The centaur did not even break stride as she entered the woods, weaving back and forth to avoid shadowed trunks. Luellan clung close to Anian. He felt low-hanging branches rake across his back. He marveled at the centaur's sleek grace as she maneuvered through the dim woodland. They climbed a hillside. Luellan was not sure he had ever been to this part of his parents' estate. Their land consisted of a quarter-million hectares of beach, moor, desert, and woodland—bounded on the east by icesea, on the west by the thirty-seven-hundred-meter peaks of the Front Range, and stretching thirty kilometers from the edge of Nyssa to the mouth of South Platte Canyon. Luellan had paid scant attention to where Anian's swift gallop had taken them. He knew, though, they must be somewhere near the southern perimeter of the estate, close to the river.

Ahead, on the hillcrest, he saw ebbing sunlight flash from white stone, silhouetting a building of grey-veined marble. At the same time, he realized Anian was no longer dodging trees; instead she ran unrestrained through a tunnel in the forest. He saw the gap was an ancient roadway. It was overgrown with grass. Short grass roots could hold in the centuries' accumulation of detritus covering the original roadbed. But the pavement was still intact underneath and was impervious to tree roots, preventing the growth of forest. The roadway led to the marble building. An *Alabaster Fortress,* he thought whimsically, and wondered what the building had actually been. He could not remember anyone mentioning it. Already he was intrigued.

Anian stopped running abruptly, planting her hooves firmly beneath her. They gouged long rents through grass and thin topsoil to expose archaic pavement beneath. An ornate permasteel gate barred the road, spanning the gap in a native stone wall. A granite obelisk stood near. It carried a plaque of corroded bronze whose lettering was obscured by verdigris crystals. The white building was beyond. It was about five stories high, with tall, narrow windows deeply recessed into slits in its marble walls.

Anian stood perfectly still. Breath whistled noisily from her wide-flared nostrils. Her flanks quivered. She held her tail arched high and stamped her front hooves.

"What's the matter? Is there something unnatural here?"

"I had forgotten," she said in a deep-throated voice. "It has been so long." She shook her head. "But how could I have forgotten such a place?"

"What had you forgotten?" His curiosity was aroused. "Tell me. You know this place? You have been to this Alabaster Fortress before?"

Anian reared up on her hind legs and wheeled around.

"Wait!" Luellan shouted. "Why must we leave? I want to explore a bit, look around. We have time."

"I *had* forgotten," she muttered through clenched teeth.

"What do you fear?" he asked, as she bolted down the ancient road. "What is this place?"

Anian did not answer. Her hooves threw chunks of sod into the air behind them. Or if she did answer, her words were lost to wind. Luellan had to cling tight to keep from being thrown from the bounding centaur's back.

As darkness deepened, they raced through the woods. Air cooled with night. Luellan found himself more and more disturbed by the old building. What secrets could it hold? he thought. There was some reason Anian would not linger there. Although he could not be sure twilight had not played tricks with perception, in the instant before Anian had bolted, he thought he had glimpsed something move behind one of the discolored windows. The after-image that persisted in his memory was one of a face: skin pastel blue like acrylic plastic, eyes sharp as broken glass. A face I have seen before, he thought, but where? In what nightmare? A face he should know.

There were no answers in the wind, only lost fragments of a wolf's plaintive howl.

2

As Luellan entered the house, he heard a loud voice coming from the solarium. Someone was arguing, by the tone of the voice, but he could not distinguish the words clearly. He walked silently down the hall, darted quickly past an open doorway, and climbed quietly up a staircase. A balcony overlooked the solarium. Now it was dark with shadow. He could watch surreptitiously from there.

The solarium was illuminated by a light fountain in its center. Luminescent fluid sprayed into streams of radiance, which coalesced into a shimmering pool. Bonsai almost a thousand years old stood in ornate granite planters. Saraltr reclined upon a gnarled trunk that had been sculpted over the years to conform to her body. She was unchanging. The tree was more malleable and would warp slowly over long periods of time. Petraltr lounged in his own tree. Neither of them wore clothing. They looked like wood nymphs: skin tanned brown as tree bark, high cheekbones, sharp noses, eyes bright as flecked agate, long supple fingers adorned with rings set with singing stones, smooth muscles, cruel lips. They had a physiologic age of thirty; normal aging had been slowed to an imperceptible rate. So they remained young and vigorous, though their chronologic age was measured in centuries. Luellan had often wondered lately what it would be like to be older than one's parents. He would soon know, if the same fate happened to him that happened to the other children of the third generation.

The loud voice he had heard came from a man he did not recognize who stood between his parents' trees, facing Saraltr. There were dark hollows around his eyes. His cloak was grimy and tattered. He held both hands extended in front of him. There was a fine tremor in his fingers.

"You can see, can't you," he said. His voice held wrongness in it. "Look at my hands." He watched the sonic sapphire Saraltr wore dangling between her breasts on an iridium chain. Blue fire crackled from the arms of the star within the stone. The subsonics emanating were too faint for Luellan to feel. But he knew the man would be perturbed by them. His voice rose again: "I have no time left, no time at all. You can see that. Do you think I would come here begging otherwise." He laughed without mirth. "Do you think I've forgotten. I'm not that bad yet."

"Nor have I forgotten," Saraltr said. She ran her fingers along her bare leg from calf to thigh. Sonic jewelry glittered. "But that's not the reason I must say no. Not even I am that hard." She smiled, showing her teeth. "Though you may think otherwise. No, I can't take the risk you ask. Five years is too long to take that chance."

"Only two years. The crystal has already been growing three. I only overestimated by two years." The tremor in his fingers increased. He closed his hands into fists and held them clenched at his sides.

"No matter." She laughed. Her singing sapphire spun about its vertical axis, casting bizarre patterns of light on her breasts. "Two years or five. Both are too long for me to wait. I won't take that chance." She lay back in the lap of her bonsai. Her head rested against gnarled bark that yielded like a living cushion. "I won't let myself get into your position, Dandarl."

"Then what am I to do?" His voice carried despair. But underneath there was something else. Luellan had not heard despair in the voice of one of his parents' friends before. Their usual mood was mild amusement.

"Try someone else." Petraltr spoke for the first time. There was laughter in his eyes.

"I have no time. Saraltr is my only chance. Yours will be the next crystal to mature, and even it will come too late for me."

"Have you thought of hybridization?" There was a snicker in Petraltr's voice. "Manimals seem unaffected so far. Something about hybrid vigor, isn't it?"

"You know I've thought of it. But the idea is repugnant to me. Hybridization is a one-way process. There is no coming back. Besides, there may not even be time to complete the process."

"Then you have only one more choice, do you not?" Petraltr smiled. "Two years with Lady Blue shouldn't be so bad." He appositioned his fingertips and looked through the spread fingers as if peering out of a cage. "Her other children have waited longer than that."

Dandarl forced a shrill laugh through taut lips. "Yes, I thought of Lady Blue," he said. "I even went to visit her a few days ago." He shuddered. "Where do you think I found the humility to ask Saraltr for a favor." Dandarl turned and walked across the solarium. When he reached the door, he called back over his shoulder: "Did you think I have not seen her children?" Then he was gone.

Luellan's parents were quiet. Saraltr closed her eyes. Petraltr continued to stare through his spread fingers.

"He has not lost his pride," he said.

"He will eventually," she answered without opening her eyes. "He lacks the foresight necessary to remain proud. He will try something desperate then." Light from her singing sapphire flickered across the foliage of bonsai. Water splashed from the fountain.

Luellan crept away, then went directly to his room. He lay on his bed, but could not sleep. He had wanted to ask his parents about the marble building he had found with Anian. But he had not wanted to let them know he had witnessed their confrontation with Dandarl. Now he was not sure he should say anything to them about the strange building.

For a long time, he stared at the bright stars visible through his room's persplex dome. He wondered why Dandarl wanted to use his mother's synthecortex crystal. What was his hurry to be integrated to mindmech? Second generation immortals were normally in a hurry over nothing; they had all the time in the world. But for some reason, Dandarl could not wait. Some change was occurring. Was that why Saraltr was unwilling to delay her own integration? He was terrified when he thought of both Saraltr and Petraltr gone to mindmech, leaving him alone to wait for the death he knew would soon come to him as it did to the others of the third generation. Why couldn't his parents recognize that fear?

Before he slept, he thought of a strange woman called Lady Blue, and remembered snatches of a song his sister used to sing. His parents told Dandarl to sleep with Lady Blue, with her other children. He did not understand the allusion. But the last line of the song ran over and over in his mind: *with eyes of ice.*

When sleep finally came, it was disturbed by dreams.

In the dark, a scream muffled by a pillow filters through night.

A roar: loud enough to strike fissures in the icesea; louder than icebergs shattering from a glacier's edge.

Ice: smooth, blue-mirrored, shimmering with light caught in the facets of cracks coalescing into a silver needle, itself curving up and blending into grey sky.

Far away a wolfpack hunts: grey ghosts drifting across the icesea, as though blown before the wind, driven south by fierce winter storms of *fimbulvetr.*

A boy shuffles across a slippery surface. From behind, the roar comes again. Cracks form through the glassine surface beneath his feet, but provide no traction. Ice creaks and groans. He looks back. A frost-giant strides after him—sure-footed on the treacherous surface, with whiskers of steel wire and eyes tourmaline bright. Icicle fingers grasp close enough so he can hear them screak together. Then another roar, with foul breath rushing past, breath too cold to frost in air—cold enough to send an ache deep in his bones.

The boy tries to run faster, but if he pushes too hard with his feet they slip on the ice. He must do something. In another moment the frost-giant will be upon him. He cuts sharply to the right, but in so doing his feet slip from under him, and he sprawls prone. He starts to push himself back up, then pauses, transfixed by what he sees within the ice: the faces of aged children, smiling like bright, ancient monkeys, with skin as translucent as parchment, showing a reticulum of blue veins beneath. Yet they are distorted by intervening fracture planes into composites—the eyes of one are transposed with the mouth of another; ears are mismatched; noses are displaced. But all are so terribly old. One he notices in particular. There is disturbing familiarity to it. A bust of a girl. But it is imperfect statuary, like a relic recovered from ruins; the nose is sheared cleanly; one ear is fragmented; the skin is as smooth as polished marble; eyes are bright with crystals of ice.

The giant looms over him, standing motionless. The boy pushes upright and turns to face him. A smile opens across the huge face to reveal blue teeth as sharp and jagged as shards of crystalline air. He bends near, smiling. Cold whistles from iron nostrils. The boy screams when he feels it touch his face. His vision dims as the cold frosts over his eyes, turning them sky-blue as their corneas opacify into crumbling eggshell.

In the dark, he screamed again.

A door whispered open. Bare feet padded across the floor, claws clicking on polished wood.

The nanny paused. Starlight shone from her sleek grey fur. Her eyes were dilated wide, with only a narrow margin of white sclera surrounding midnight blue pupils. Long canine teeth flashed white. She looked at the boy lying in bed, then climbed in with him, pulling a sheer covering over them. Smooth fabric slid coldly over her fur. The boy lay on his back, staring into darkness.

"A dream?" she asked. "Did a nightmare wake my little man?"

Luellan did not answer at first, letting his breathing quiet instead. Sweat cooled on his skin. "Will he return every night to haunt me?"

"If he does, I'll always be here to comfort you." She moved her hand close to his face, but did not touch it. There was webbing between her fingers. "I'll protect you from the giant of your dreams."

"There were children living in the ice this time."

Her breathing paused. Nostrils closed tight, then dilated. "What ice?" Vestigial ears perked forward.

"In the frozen sea. Near the gravshute. And they were old. The way people once became before they died. The way Lorriel became before she left. Why is it that only children age now? How is it possible to be both old and young? Why are the elderly all children?"

"Anything is possible in dreams." She drew him closer, feeling his warmth pulled into her body. His hands absently stroked the fur in the hollow between scapula and buttock.

"You once lived in the cold water beneath the icesea," he said, "with the other nereids. Did you find the children of the third generation there? Is that where they went? Is that where I'll be sent?"

The nanny said nothing.

"What is it that makes me so terrified of the frost-giant? Why do I need to run away from him?" He let his hand drift over her buttock, to smooth the soft fur along the back of her thigh. "There's some quality about him I sense during the dream that later fades from memory. I can't recall why I should be so scared."

She felt muscles tighten beneath his skin. He was becoming lean and angular as adolescence neared. She said nothing.

"Lorriel had the same dream, didn't she?" His eyes used to tear when he thought of his sister, but now her loss no longer hurt as intensely, lingering instead as a cold ache. "She sometimes told me about the frost-giant who awakened her at night. I remember she was in a strange melancholia then, and prone to weeping for no reason, and her speech was affected by heavy profundity." He looked into the nanny's eyes. "*They* told me she went away, but they wouldn't say where she went. And Lorriel never came to say goodbye. She would have done that, had she wanted to go." The boy bit his lip, chewing on a ragged edge of tissue. "You know where she is, don't you? *You* would know where your grandchildren are."

"Don't say that." Nictitating membranes closed over her eyes.

"It's true, isn't it. I mean, Lorriel and I are your grandchildren."

"Only in a manner of speaking."

"You are first generation. You are genoparent to Petraltr and Saraltr."

"Only because our genomes share certain genes. *She* is gone. *Her* persona has left to become part of mindmech. Only shadows linger, to haunt *me* with their ancient passions. *I'm* young and new. Exorcism has rid me of *her* schemes. You would not have liked her much. Not as you like me."

"But do you know where Lorriel is?"

"She was my closest friend. We grew up together. I am only a few years older than she. I miss her very much."

"Then you know where she went."

Her silence was affirmation.

"And the others, are they at the same place? When I was very young, I remember playing with other children. They were all older than I though; I was always the youngest. But when they reached a certain age, they no longer came to play with the rest of us, until only Lorriel and I were left, and then she too went away. But before they left, each one seemed to develop a pensive, moody melancholia. They would sit alone and sing an old, sad song to themselves in voices so low the words could not be understood. But mood could be felt—blue depression." He spread his hands in front, examining his fingers. "That same melancholia now hangs before me." He closed his eyes, remembering images of ice, and heard again the ponderous footfalls of the frost-giant. "I remember how dark and gaunt their eyes became from sleeplessness. A strange coldness was in their voices when they spoke of the terrible giant stalking their dreams. Do you hear ice in mine?" He lay back, eyes open, and began to hum a melody. "Do you know the words?" he asked. "Do you know why Lady Blue hurts so much, why she has eyes of ice?"

"Where did you hear that song?"

"Lorriel sang it once a long time ago. And Anian sang it tonight. Can you sing it too?"

"Not now. There will be time enough later." She touched her hand to his abdomen, making circles with her fingertips, saying nothing more.

"Will I be going to join the others?" he asked. "Will I sing of Lady Blue then?"

"Maybe," she said, moving her hand to touch sparse new pubic hair. "Only you will know when that time comes."

"It's lonely being the only one left."

She brought his hand to cup her breast, pushing the nipple between his fingers. She touched his penis. "How do you suppose I'll feel," she said.

3

The nanny was gone when Luellan awoke. The persplex dome overhead had opacified to block most of the sun's heat, yet still his room was filled with soft sunlight. Awakening came slowly: he savored the hiatal feeling between sleep and wakefulness, when night-dreams lost their terror and could be glimpsed again with detached amusement, knowing one need only open one's eyes to vanquish their demons. A face lingered in memory to disturb him still. The face he had glimpsed behind the window of the marble building he saw again in his dreams. And he could not be sure which was real and which was fantasy, or if either had substance. He closed his eyes. Her remembered image was still vivid: opalescent skin, eyes blue as cobalt flame. Then the face faded as he woke. For a moment he felt sad. He had a silly urge to weep.

He jumped out of bed, thinking of the mysterious building he had discovered and his vow to find out more about it. Time was wasting. He could not afford the luxury of self-pity.

He showered quickly, skin tingling as jets of ultrasound peeled a thin layer of epidermis away. He thought of the building again. He could not decide if it or the face within intrigued him more. From its appearance, it could have been built in pre-recombinant times. Luellan shivered, thinking of that tempestuous period, when genetic change had to be left to the slow vagaries of natural selection. Each person then lived for such a brief span, only long enough to fuse one or two or several of his gametes with those of another, in the brave hope that by random chance the mingling of DNA would produce a better combination, when it was just as likely to produce a worse one. After the recombinant revolution, there was no need for further trial-and-error exercises—each individual's genome was carefully constructed and represented the optimal pattern of DNA molecules. A short life-span, necessary for the forces of natural selection to operate, was no longer needed. Indeed, the genes responsible for predetermined senescence had been repressed, so previous "natural" aging no longer occurred. Freed from degenerative disease, there was no finite limit to the human life-span. Practical immortality had been attained. Provided one could avoid natural hazards and trauma, one could live in perpetual youth indefinitely. Or at least the first and second recombinant generations could. Luellan belonged to the third. There was something wrong with his generation.

For five hundred years following the revolution, there had been no new individuals nor need for any: each member of the first generation had a defined role in society for which he was ideally suited. Yet even though individuals did not age, society was still subject to entropy— there were still accidents; people underwent hybridization to manimals; minds became integrated to mindmech and their former bodies became cyborgs, *mech,* more efficient workers than ordinary machines. Eventually the need for replacements occurred. No system could remain entirely static. Saraltr and Petraltr were members of the second recombinant generation. The new steady-state lasted over five hundred years. But dynamic change continued to occur. Entropy could only be attenuated. More replacements were needed. Now a different mechanism was used. Mindmech decided the third generation should be conceived naturally, without benefit of genetic engineering. *A grand experiment,* some said. *Dangerous folly,* said others. But the motives of mindmech were inscrutable. Perhaps it was trying to maintain reproductive potential. Maybe it was attempting to promote hybrid vigor. Motives did not matter. Because Luellan was the last member of the third generation. Something had gone wrong. Some mistake had occurred. Mindmech had made a miscalculation. The children that had come before him had all been afflicted with a strange malady when they reached puberty—they aged at a tremendously accelerated rate. They had all been sent away. Where they were now, Luellan was not certain, nor would his parents tell him when he asked.

He pushed morbid thoughts aside, determined not to brood away the day as he was prone to lately. He dressed quickly, deciding to wear only a spidersilk burnoose. He fastened it around his neck with a platinum clasp studded with singing stones.

As he was leaving, he decided his mouth tasted stale. He chewed an amoebiclean tablet. Bioengineered amoebae, dormant in the dry tablet, were activated by his saliva, and hungrily devoured any tartar or food particles adherent to his teeth. He had to chew a tablet about once a week to replenish the amoebae. A pleasant mint taste lingered in his mouth.

The nanny was waiting for him in the kitchen, alerted by housemind that he was up. He dutifully kissed her furry cheek and suffered through her daily inspection of whether he had bathed and dressed properly. Only then did she allow him to sit down for breakfast.

Sharlyn brought him food freshly prepared by the kitchen: internal sensors allowed the housemind to monitor the movements of its inhabitants and anticipate their desires. Lately Luellan had had little appetite or interest in food, despite elaborate attempts by the kitchen to tempt him with interesting cuisine. Today he felt different; he was hungry. He quickly devoured fruit crepes and vegetable omelets, interrupting his eating only to gulp apple juice noisily.

Sharlyn sat across from him, eating a grapefruit half and sipping a cup of aromatic tea. She wore a simple gown of saffron linen, with billowed sleeves and a rope belt clasped around the waist. Sunlight streamed through the leaves of wallplants to be caught in her fur. A single singing pearl was suspended from pseudograv studs piercing each ear flap. Her fingers were long and supple, tipped with retractable claws and with transparent skin webbed between them. Her pupils were vertical slits in azure irises; her face was flushed with youth. Now she was a young governess. A long time ago her former personality had attempted to overcome ennui with hybridization to a nereid: mammalian phage virus was used to insert seal DNA into each of her cells. She had been genetically engineered into a hybrid of human and seal. Her kind had been adapted to live beneath the antarctic seas. A new race had been created. A new life waited to be lived. But even the novelty of the subsea colonies palled. Her interest faded. Boredom returned. Nereids were no more interesting than humans. Less so, not having developed a taste for decadence yet. Twenty years ago her previous mind had succumbed to boredom and undergone integration to mindmech. A new persona had been allowed to develop over twenty years. Her present mind was only that old. Though her body had a chronological age measured in centuries, she still appeared no more than twenty years old, and physiologically was no older, since cellular aging did not occur.

It occurred to Luellan she might know something of the building he had discovered.

"Sharlyn," he said, swallowing a bite of crepe.

"Yes, child." She smiled, knowing how it irritated him to be reminded of their relative status.

"How well do you know this estate?"

Nictitating membranes closed her eyes. Her forehead furrowed. "Fairly well, I imagine. I suppose *she'd* been most everywhere one time or another. Those memories are still partially available, though they're dim now. Why do you ask?"

"What do you know of a marble building in the southwest corner, in the foothills near the river?"

She looked at him carefully. "When were you there?"

"Last night. While riding Anian."

"A shame. Anian knows better. Unless the silly nag wasn't thinking. She does tend to have lapses of memory."

"Then you do know what it is? Tell me. Does someone live there?"

Her eyes darkened. Pupils widened briefly. "No, no one lives there now. It's just an old building from times past. Better it should have been torn down long ago."

"But what was it used for?"

"Nothing important." She looked at him with a stern expression. "Petraltr would be upset if he knew you'd been there. Better he should never know."

Luellan understood her intimation and was quiet. But he did not intend to drop the matter, either. Now he was even more intrigued by the marble building. But he did not finish his breakfast that morning, either.

In the mornings, icewind blew. Cold air that collected over the icesea at night was pulled overland by updrafts rising from the Front

Range, producing an easterly wind. With evening, the flow was reversed and a western chinook wind blew, when warm air once more pooled over the great expanse of ice.

Luellan walked along the beach. Wind pulled his hair streaming out behind. The sand was as hard as pavement, cemented by melted ice crystals carried by the wind. Ahead lay a boathouse. It was a low structure built into the side of a moor, looking more a bunker than an anchorage.

Inside the air was still, but ice crystals could be heard scouring the outside walls. Luellan opened a locker, removed a pair of space-coveralls, and pulled them on. They fit skin tight. The sheer white fabric from which they were sewn was almost a perfect insulator. Its permeability to his body heat could be varied by changes in a minute energy field carried on each strand of cloth. The coveralls would maintain a uniform inside temperature of 37° C, despite ambient temperature extremes of near absolute zero to several thousand degrees. Originally designed to be worn in space before sailors were bioengineered, they worked equally well in harsh terrestrial environments.

He opened the outside door. Wind swirled inside. He detached the moorings of the iceboat and pushed it out on the ice. Metal blades screaked on grit embedded in the ice. The iceboat was of ancient design: three running blades mounted on a T frame, with the trailing single blade connected via its vertical axis to a tiller and able to rotate about that axis to provide steering. A silver permaplastic shell provided a streamlined cowling surrounding the sailor. It looked much like a giant, three-legged water strider. Luellan stepped the mast and secured its three support cables to the end of each arm of the T and its base. Next he attached the boom to the mast. The sail was wound on a roller inside the hollow boom. He started the sail-guides in their groove in the mast. Then, holding tiller and boom line in one hand, he furled the sail with the other. Wind caught in its crimson fabric and billowed the sail taut. The iceboat lurched forward, then steadied and raced along the ice parallel to the beach. Luellan gradually increased his angle of attack to the wind and headed out to sea. Far away, silhouetted on the horizon, was the space needle, curving into the sky like an ancient rocket's contrail that it replaced.

When he was safely away from shore, Luellan hiked out in a trapeze, using his own weight to keep the windward blade from hopping because of lateral force. He hung suspended by webbing attached to the mast, and braced his feet against the cowling. An extension of the tiller handle allowed him to steer with one hand. He held the boom line in the other.

High above, a whisperbird soared, buffeted by turbulence. Its wings were outstretched with their terminal feathers fanning out like fingers. Clawed feet were held close to its body. He imagined what the iceboat must look like from its viewpoint: red sail billowing above a shiny silver hull suspended between two water strider struts.

Luellan wondered if it was Alelis, his other aunt. As a baby, he had been tended by the great whisperbird. She would take him flying with her. He hung suspended beneath her in netting she clutched tightly in her talons. They would soar for hours high above the ground. She would sing him ancient ballads about bird-heroes. He had absolute trust in her. Never for a moment did it occur to him that her grip might weaken and she might drop him. He had been as content to hang a thousand meters above the ground in a net carried by a huge, malformed bird as he was to crawl about the floor of his nursery. More content. Warm wind was soothing. Her low voice lulled him to sleep. He came to love the whisperbird like a mother. But eventually he grew too heavy for her to carry. And a whisperbird was not made to hop about on the ground. So he had to content himself to watch her as she soared, and wish that he could join her in her hunt.

Now again he watched a whisperbird drifting in the high air currents. He briefly longed to soar beside her. Then he remembered his plan and the longing faded. Today he would discover the secret of the Alabaster Fortress. He was sure he could reach it from the icesea.

He sailed to the south, almost flying before the icewind. Ice screamed beneath sharp blades as crystals collapsed, melted, and turned to vapor. The gas formed a thin film beneath the runners, lifted them from the surface, and reduced friction to almost nothing. Sail fabric billowed, snapped taut. Rigging sang in the wind. Permaplastic bent and creaked. The iceboat hit speeds over one hundred kilometers per hour before gusts of icewind.

Twenty miles away was the mouth of the South Platte River. His Alabaster Fortress lay inland along the river.

Before long he was abreast of the river's mouth. He could see the deep canyon where the river tumbled out of a gap in the mountains. In the foothills, the river had long ago cut a broad valley. Now the river too was frozen where its flow was less. Open water did not start until the fast, white-water was reached. He could sail his iceboat almost all the way to Waterton Canyon.

Luellan brought the boat about and ran before the wind. He locked the tiller in place and furled his spinnaker. Wind billowed it full. A huge hawk was woven with contrasting colored thread on the spinnacker. As it opened, the hawk's wings became outspread; its claws extended wide. Beneath the raptor was lettering spelling the iceboat's name: *Kestrel*.

From above came a harsh cry. Luellan looked up. The cry came again, louder. The whisperbird was dropping: she had tucked her wings close to her body, using them only for guidance, and the great clawed toes were spread wide. The hunting scream sounded: a long raspy whistle. How well Luellan remembered. He watched enthralled as she fell from the sky, not realizing what she hunted. Like all manimals, whisperbirds were prone to have the human component of their minds suppressed by the animal. Human awareness would drift into subconsciousness, lulled there by simple animalistic pleasure. The creature would then react instinctively, unrestrained by reason or logic.

The whisperbird screamed again. Luellan could see her clearly now: sulfur eyes, black beak, blue claws, purple-speckled breast feathers ruffed by wind. It was Alelis. But she was attacking him, he realized belatedly.

She hit the spinnaker hard, tearing long rents in its fabric with her claws, before the cloth bunched beneath her toes and held. She clutched tightly to it, slashing with her beak.

Luellan released the boom line, allowing the boom to swing away from the wind and spill air from the mainsail. At the same time, he loosened the spinnaker line so it would flop free. Next he dropped the friction brake; it dug deep grooves in the ice. The iceboat gradually slowed to a stop. All the time, Alelis continued to tear at the spinnaker fabric.

Luellan jumped from the iceboat as it stopped. He bunched sailcloth in his hands and caught the whisperbird in folds of fabric. With her wings and legs pinned, he spoke softly to her, calming her. The wild jabs of her beak subsided. He felt her muscles relax. She no longer strained against him. He released her from the tangles of spinnaker cloth, then sat on the iceboat's railing. She hopped over and sat on his thigh. Her claws pressed through his coveralls, but could not pierce the tough fabric. He stroked her feathers and crooned to her from deep in his throat.

She answered, singing a song so low he only felt the vibrations in her throat like a cat purring. After a bit she spoke: "It's too easy to let the bird come to the surface." Her voice was raspy, her words bent by a hybrid larynx. "But such joy! If only you could know the thrill of dropping so swiftly through the air—the wondrous joy of not thinking." She cocked her head to the side and watched him with yellow eyes. "How is my little boy? Not so little anymore. You've grown so large. Will I never again take you flying?"

"Only if I sprout wings like yours."

"Then you should. There is peace to be found amidst the high air currents. There is solace drifting in the wind. I could show you things you would not believe." She began again to sing songs from long ago, telling him of bird-heroes, of ancient battles fought in the air.

Luellan lost track of time as he listened to her sing. It brought back happy memories of when he could fly with her. He remembered how different the land appeared from high in the air, the insignificance it took on. When at last she bade farewell and took wing it was almost dark. The wind had shifted. A warm sundowner blew strongly from the mountains.

With a start, Luellan realized he would never make it to the river's mouth before dark now. He was directly downwind from Waterton Canyon. The river was not wide enough to allow him to tack against the wind. He had planned to use the favorable direction the icewind blew to gain egress to the canyon. It was too late for that tactic now.

He furled the mainsail and headed back home, easily quartering into the westerly wind. Something disturbed him about Alelis. She had watched him sail the iceboat with spinnaker furled many times before. Never previously had she mistakenly attacked *Kestrel*. Why today? What had provoked her? When he finally saw the glowing dome of his house, the answer came to him. He remembered then the song she sang deep in her throat when he had first calmed her. He had felt those vibrations before. They were the same; she sang the same song he had felt in the centaur's throat, the same song Lorriel had sung to herself.

Now he remembered a little more of the words: *Lady of death, refuses to die. / Lady of night, who lived twice. / Lady of pain, too old to cry. / Lady Blue, with eyes of ice.* But the meaning was still hidden from him. And why did Alelis want to keep him away from the Alabaster Fortress? What terrible secret was hidden there? How were his own dark dreams linked to the ancient Lady Blue? He thought if he could remember more of the words of the song, understanding would come. But he could not. There must be answers to be found within the old marble building.

He vowed to seek them out.

4

In night, the frost-giant again troubled his sleep.

In morning, the reason for his fear was forgotten, again.

Luellan decided to see if he could find out anything about the marble building on his parents' estate. There were records kept in the library. An hour's search failed to reveal anything of significance. But he did find an interesting monograph on molecular biology; dogma upon which the recombinant revolution was based.

Multicolored fire played across the surface of the memory crystal, and was mirrored in Luellan's eyes as he stared intently deep inside the stone. Images flickered too fast to be consciously perceived, yet they formed subliminal impressions, to be remembered later as the need arose. He was unaware of the actual learning process; all he had to do was maintain a trancelike concentration. The memory crystal was a rudimentary matrix of synthecortex; too simple to contain a complete persona, as the linked crystals of mindmech did, but complex enough to store the memories of several experts of a particular discipline, in regard to their subject. When the crystal finished flashing, Luellan would have had an experience equivalent to years of intensive study.

The basics had already been presented. Now he was learning about the techniques of genetic engineering: Mammalian oncogenic viruses had been adapted to carry new genetic material to cells' nuclei, as well as excise unwanted genes. Instead of carrying DNA that transformed a cell into a cancerous one, the viruses could be made to carry a gene of the genosurgeon's choosing. With the use of these domesticated phage viruses, human genomes could be manipulated as easily as bacterial genes had been for years previously with the use of bacteriophage and plasmids. The artificial placenta allowed genoengineered zygotes to develop into viable fetuses that eventually became healthy infants. The genes that caused susceptability to disease were excised; there were no more heart attacks, cancer, crippling arthritis, diabetes, high blood pressure, or strokes. People could live in perfect health.

Yet even in the absence of disease, aging continued. The maximal human life-span was not appreciably extended. One hundred years was still about as long as one could live. Death still occurred then. The early genosurgeons were perplexed. There seemed no solution to death. They recalled an earlier observation called the Hayflick phenomenon— there seemed to be a finite number of times a nonmalignant cell could divide. After fifty-nine cellular divisions, the cells died. Death was preprogrammed, an inevitable event coded in the DNA of the cell. Only cancerous transformation could circumvent this scheduled senescence. But there was no more cancer. It had been excised from the population. The genosurgeons had to resurrect cancer victims that had been held in cryogenic suspended animation. They studied them and did find the solution to inevitable death locked in their DNA. Immortality had been perfected.

As the crystal was almost finished, Luellan noticed a familiar name had been mentioned: Lady Blue. But he had missed in what context her name had been used. As he was scanning back to find where she appeared, voices intruded, like insect buzzings, disturbing his concentration. He tried to ignore them, but the act of ignoring diverted his attention from the crystal. He could not maintain the proper trance. It was broken; light died within the stone; as his attention wavered, a retinal reflex feedback loop was interrupted. He massaged his eyes through closed eyelids, until red flame blazed in his mind. Still the voices buzzed. He recognized them as those of his parents, but could not understand their meaning.

They came from outside, through a plantwall. Luellan moved closer to the wall, sitting on a fungoid bench. He made a gap by pushing aside shrubbery and peered through. His parents were sunning together on the sun deck, lying close to each other on silk pads. Their skins were tanned the same deep bronze. Both were beaded with sweat sparkling in sunlight. Petraltr had sharply defined musculature—a physique that was molded from classic sculpture. His angular face was framed by reddish curls of hair. Saraltr had finer features and softer muscles. She had the same amber eyes as Anian. Her face had sharp cheekbones. Their voices came to him clearly now.

"We can put off integration a little longer," Petraltr said, "it won't be much longer now before he reaches puberty. We can't take him to Lady Blue before the time comes. We'll have to wait a little longer."

"You can, but I can't," Saraltr answered, holding her hands out in front of her. There was a fine tremor in her fingers.

Petraltr watched her closely. "When did that develop?" he asked.

She shrugged. "This morning. But it doesn't matter. My neurocrystal is ready now. I would have had to undergo integration soon anyway. If the matrix of synthecortex is not stabilized by organized thought, entropic decay will soon begin. You know it takes five years to grow a proper crystal. They are quite expensive and are not incubated casually. I can't wait five more years." She looked at her fingers. "There is no time left. I don't want to be in the same predicament as Dandarl. We knew five years ago this would happen."

"But that was when we thought Luellan would be . . ." He paused.

"I know. It was just after we realized what had gone wrong with the third generation children." She laughed hollowly. "Who would have thought he would have delayed puberty. He should have begun the change a year ago. But I can't wait for him. You know that."

"I know. But it seems unfair to him. We can't both leave him."

"No, we can't leave him. There's another choice."

"Before the change. We can't do that."

"There is no other way. I want you to take him to Lady Blue before my integration. I do not want him to die alone." She closed her fingers one at a time to make two fists. "But I can't wait for him."

Luellan let the leaves fall back into place. He felt a cold ache deep inside. Had they taken Lorriel to Lady Blue? Is that where she had gone? And what did it mean to go to her? He remembered vividly Lorriel's progeria, her weeping, her raging fits of anger. It had taken him a long time to forgive her, to understand her cruelty was not intentional. But he still carried scars to remind him, to prevent complete forgiving. He felt dread apprehension. Sweat formed on his palms. What did Lady Blue do to children?

Somehow he knew the marble building held the connection he sought. And there was only one way to discover what it was.

Anian was grazing leisurely in the orchard when Luellan found her. She would nibble for a bit on young, tender shoots of grass growing at the trees' bases, then rear up daintily on her hind legs to snatch a pear or an apple from an overhanging branch. As he neared, she looked up and whinnied recognition, but continued to graze. Luellan approached her cautiously—when she grazed, sometimes horse-thoughts pushed her human persona deep beneath the surface and she would instinctively act like a horse and run away when he tried to catch her. So he spoke soothingly, reassuring her he meant no harm. She stood still, muscles taut, but allowed him to come near and stroke her neck and flanks. Gradually she relaxed and turned to nuzzle his ear.

He grasped a handful of mane and pulled himself astride her back, then gently prodded her sides with his heels. She cantered through the orchard. He kicked her harder; her pace quickened to a gallop. She weaved through the trees, cutting close to their trunks like a quarterhorse trained to barrel race. Luellan had to duck to avoid being brushed off by overhanging branches.

"Go, girl," he yelled, "run like the wind!"

Soon they were through the orchard and entered open pasture. He touched her cheek, heading her to the south. "Take me where the Alabaster Fortress stands," he whispered in her ear.

They galloped with smooth, effortless grace over grass meadows, across clear brooks, plunging down into deep ravines and then clambering up their steep sides. To the east lay the icesea shimmering blue with reflected sunlight. On the eastern horizon, the great space needle curved toward the west, up which gravships catapulted into orbit. To the west were darkly timbered slopes and the snow-capped thirty-seven-hundred-meter peaks of the Front Range.

Soon they ran along the banks of the South Platte. Far ahead were the ruins of an ancient dam that once spanned the river, backing water deep into the mountains. The Alabaster Fortress was in those mountains. Soon Luellan would know what secrets it held.

They raced down a wide meadow. Luellan sensed movement in his peripheral vision. He turned to look into the trees on the east side of the meadow. A grey shape darted through the woods, paralleling their course. He felt the hair at the nape of his neck rise, remembering lonely howls echoing down steep mountain valleys at night.

Knowing it had been seen, the wolf left the concealment of the woods and loped along the edge of the meadow. Luellan saw that it intended to intercept them. At the same time, Anian noticed the wolf. Her mind was mostly occupied with horse-thoughts and she reacted as a horse would—with blind panic. She turned perpendicular to their previous path and bolted toward the foothills. The wolf turned also and began chasing them. Anian headed toward the mouth of a ravine that opened into the meadow. Luellan spoke soothingly to her, trying to calm her. But her human mind was too deeply buried to hear him. She entered the canyon and ran madly along its sandy bottom, scattering rocks with her hooves.

Behind, the wolf followed, running silently with long, fluid strides. Luellan clung tightly to Anian, still whispering to her, trying to reach that part of her mind that was buried beneath primeval terror. But with no effect; they continued their headlong plunge up the ravine, climbing ever higher into the foothills. They splashed through pools of rain water that had collected in erosion basins in red sandstone ledges.

Sunlight was caught and held in tumid drops of water suspended briefly in midair, before they splattered on both sides of the canyon, wetting granular rock walls like spatters of blood. Anian's hooves thudded into sand, clattered on bare rock, and skittered through gravel. Her breath whistled through flared nostrils. Lather dripped from her muzzle and sprayed along her sides to coat her legs with sticky foam.

The wolf gradually outdistanced them, narrowed the gap between them. Even Luellan could hear the sound of its paws now—like a winter wind drifting corn snow through spindly branches. Anian's ears pricked up and her pace quickened.

The canyon made a sharp turn to the right. Anian cut close enough to the rock wall that Luellan's leg brushed against it. Pain shot all along his right side. Her hooves slipped a little in the sand. Beyond the curve, the canyon ended abruptly in a sheer sandstone face with spring water oozing from pores in the rock. They were trapped by a dead-end box canyon.

Anian wheeled around, kicking sand high. Already the wolf had turned the corner and stood before them, to hold the centaur at bay. Her sides heaved. Her eyes were wide. She reared up, bracing her rump against the rock wall, waving her forelegs in front.

The wolf spoke: "Settle down, Anian. Don't you know me?" His voice was deep and growling, but clear, with the words precisely formed.

Anian stayed reared back on her hind legs.

Luellan spoke soothingly in her ear: "There's nothing to fear from a wolfman."

"Remember the times we've spent playing on the beach," the wolf said, "with me chasing you, close to your heels, then you turning to chase me. You must remember the time I pulled that mad cat from your back."

Luellan felt the centaur start to relax. She dropped her forefeet to the ground and spoke: "*You* should know better than to sneak up on me like that, Dondk. You know the horse in me is sometimes too strong for the woman. You should know your genodaughter that well."

"My fault. But it could not be helped this time. You had forgotten again and were going to take the child to the house of ice."

Haltingly: "Isn't it time for him to go?" She shook her head. "No, I guess not. Sometimes it is hard to remember everything. It's difficult enough keeping track of which grass is tasty and where cool springs of water lie. So much easier not to have to think."

"*She* sent you after us," Luellan said harshly. "And you obeyed her.

The one who taught me how to stalk, who trained me to run without tiring. I thought you took pride in your independence. Why don't you stop meddling and go back to chasing rabbits." He jumped from the centaur's back, landing lightly in the sand. "Why can't you all leave me alone? I'm the one that's going to die. You're safe from that. Why can't you let me face it my own way?"

The wolfman smiled, exposing hybrid teeth that were yellowed at their roots. "There are reasons. Dyads wait. There will be answers soon." With that, he padded off.

5

Luellan followed the wolf with Anian coming along behind him. They backtracked down the canyon for a few hundred meters, then climbed out of the ravine using a narrow trail cut into sheer rock. The trail wound ever higher until finally cresting on a flat plateau. Luellan knew where they were going. It was a long time since he had last been there. He had gone with Lorriel then.

They crossed a broad flat of grass and shrubs that ended at the base of a huge spire of red sandstone jutting from the rim of the plateau. A deep pool of water, fed by springs trickling from rock, was dark and cool. A grove of bristle-cone pines circled the pool.

Anian drank noisily from the pool, then wandered away to graze.

Luellan sat on the ground next to the pool and watched his reflection on its smooth surface. Water striders skimmed across, distorting his image. Dondk flopped to the ground. His tongue hung sloppily and dripped saliva as he panted.

Luellan waited.

The trees ringing the periphery of the pool were old and gnarled, with thick trunks and twisted branches. Whorls in their bark formed the vague outline of faces, and below, lumps and swellings suggested arms and legs and a torso. The pines had been there long before the icesea formed, before there were any cities, before there were any men. They had first sprouted almost as soon as the mountains were through being thrust up from alluvial plain. They were still the world's oldest living creatures.

The air was never still on that promontory: icewind blew during the day, as cold air from over the icesea spilled into low pressure zones left by updrafts rising from the mountains; but when night came, the wind reversed and became a warm sundowner.

Wind rustled through the trees' needles. Wood resonated.

Luellan closed his eyes and listened. Dyads sang.

Their song could be heard within the wind, sung in a chorus of voices. The song was sad, almost a lamentation, evoking images of weathered old women clutching fetishes and crooning over the loss of a lover. No voice was yet distinctly separate—they blended together to produce strange harmony. He listened closely, relaxing his mind, letting sound images form. He saw conifers growing in a circle around a pool, slowly growing. Then medmech came. The pines were carefully groomed over the years. Hormones were implanted in holes drilled in their trunks. They became a stately grove. Next, a party scene: people dressed in fine silks danced, laughed, embraced, sipped wine, ate sweetmeats and crisp fruits. Then partying ceased, laughter quieted. Each person removed his garments, then stood before a tree. Medmech circulated efficiently, smearing a jelly on bare skin. Each person embraced his tree, wrapping arms and legs tightly around the trunk and hugging it. Medmech wound polymer film around each tree, enclosing the person in a transparent cocoon. Humidity misted on the surface within. A fine, blue fuzz grew on both skin and bark. Plasticizing fungus sent mycelia deep into tissues, both tree and human, and secreted enzymes that dissolved intracellular cement. Slowly the human form melded into the tree trunk, absorbed by osmotic pressure. Human cells blended into woody cortex, distributed from root to leaves, yet retaining a tenuous connection with each other by extended pseudopods; identity persisted. Yet self was augmented, as the roots of each tree entwined with those of the others, and in places had even fused together. Dual symbiosis resulted; a mingling of human bodies into trees, a joining of human minds into linkage: a sentient grove was formed, a symbiotic hybrid.

Luellan had once spent many hours resting in their shade, listening to soft harmonious singing, hearing ballads of other times and places. Sometimes one voice would be prominent and sing a particular song while the others provided a chorus. Luellan had learned to recognize each individual dyad. He sometimes wondered how much they could perceive of their external environment; they must have some dim sense, for they seemed to recognize him and respond to his presence, singing their songs for him. Lorriel had discovered the grove in one of her many explorations, and she had brought Luellan there.

A clear soprano swelled out of wind resonating across pine needles. Luellan knew the dyad's voice, but he could not remember her singing solo before. He had heard only fragments of her voice before, as she had previously remained in the background chorus.

She sang a low, blue ballad now, with unendurable hurt beneath bending notes. At first Luellan only felt aching cold. He remembered Lorriel singing. There was similarity in the voice of the dyad to that of his sister. They felt the same pain.

As his mind adapted, images again formed and told a story once forgotten:

> A girl fell sick on her wedding,
> rigors chilling to bone.
> She knew what malaise befell her,
> as all of her kin had known.
>
> Her sire carried a gene of death,
> that all his children bore.
> A gene of cancer so painful,
> they wish for life no more.
>
> But love made her foolish and brave;
> She took injections of flame.
> Chemotherapy burned deeply,
> where surgery could not maim.
>
> As long as fire flared brightly,
> coursing along in her veins,
> carcinoma was held in remission,
> chased away with its pain.
>
> Lady of death, refuses to die.
> Lady of night, who lived twice.
> Lady of pain, too old to cry.
> Lady Blue, with eyes of ice.
>
> When her lover died an old man,
> the lady was still pretty.
> Her DNA held the secret
> of immortality.

She was mother to a new race;
a new age dawned bright.
Morning laughter lasted forever;
day never became night.

But a Lady melancholy,
sang to her long dead lover.
She longed to be with him again,
foresaking lips of others.

Lonely decades passed slowly,
reason faded, skin blued.
Youth's a mask of fragile disguise,
hiding life not renewed.

Lady of death, refuses to die.
Lady of night, who lived twice.
Lady of pain, too old to cry.
Lady Blue, with eyes of ice.

A lady blue chanting her dirge;
her singing must suffice.
Frost-giants wait for their blushing bride;
Her soul is caught by ice.

Warmth fades from a lady sleeping.
She dreams of her dead beau.
Verdigris fades from skin frosted
with red helium snow.

Safely within her frozen tomb,
Lady Blue awaits her children.
They come to her old and wrinkled,
to share her painful ken.

As frost-giants roar and their wolves howl,
Lady Blue laughs inside.
Her children are safe from giant's teeth,
until winter subsides.

Lady of death, refuses to die.
Lady of night, who lived twice.
Lady of pain, too old to cry.
Lady Blue, with eyes of ice.

A splash of water roused Luellan from thought. Anian was drinking from the pool, blowing air noisily through her nostrils to keep water out. He had lost track of time while listening to the dyads sing; it was almost dark. With a start, he realized the trees were no longer singing, but he could not recall when they had stopped, nor did he know if they sang any songs other than Lady Blue's ballad. Dondk was no where to be seen.

He had become completely absorbed by the ballad of Lady Blue. He sang it to himself, knowing it would stay in his mind this time. He found the lyrics disturbing, and at the same time, satisfying. But he knew there was meaning he did not understand.

He pulled himself onto Anian's back. He stayed lost in thought as she cantered along. Only when the lights of his house neared did he remember his vow to visit the Alabaster Fortress.

A shiver tingled up his back as he remembered the pale blue face with ice eyes he had glimpsed behind its window. He knew who she must be.

6

He found his parents in the solarium, lounging in their bonsai.

"Where have you been?" Saraltr asked.

"Listening to the trees sing. Hearing their old songs."

"Did you understand?" A singing diamond quivered on her finger.

"A little. Enough."

"Then you know that you must go to Lady Blue." She made a fist. Luellan did not answer.

"You know that, don't you," Saraltr persisted. "It's for the best. There's no other way. You don't want to die, do you?"

Again Luellan was quiet.

"We hoped it would not have to be this way," Petraltr said. "But there are some things you don't understand. Once it seemed there would be plenty of time for explanations, but now there is no time left at all. Your mother's crystal is ready now." He paused, looking into Luellan's eyes. "Her waking comes tomorrow."

Luellan looked quickly to his mother, in hope of finding contradiction to what his father said. But denial was not to be found in her eyes. He ran to his room to escape the coldness in their eyes, seeking solace in sleep.

A frost-giant looms against a darkened sky. A boy runs terrified over ice. Footfalls as loud as thunder follow him; a roar paralyzes him briefly with its force, then he skitters once more across the frozen sea.

Ice shudders ahead, then drops beneath his feet, sending him sprawling. He scrambles to his feet, standing on the brink of a crevice that has just split the ice. The frost-giant comes nearer, bellowing glee when he sees his quarry trapped by the fissure.

The boy quickly decides. He has no other choice. Backing up a few paces, he attempts to leap the crevice. However, he slips on the ice as he jumps. He falls just a little short of the far bank. His body teeters on the edge, half on, half off, until finally his clutching fingers weaken. He slips into the crack in the ice.

As he falls, the jagged walls snap together, trapping him within ice. A strange tranquility soothes him. Others are near. They are smiling. He hears familiar voices, familiar songs. Lorriel touches his hand. A blue face stands behind her; crystalline eyes glitter.

Far above, the frost-giant rages, pounding fists futilely into solid ice. But the boy is safe from his temper, protected within hard, cold ice.

He felt the nanny slip into bed with him. Her fur was soft against his skin as she held him. She stroked his skin. Her claws were retracted.

"The dream again," she said.

He said nothing.

"The dyads sang you the ballad of Lady Blue today."

"Why couldn't you just have told me?"

"Sometimes it's difficult to speak of things. We didn't want you to worry." Her nostrils closed for a moment, then opened with a rush of breath. Almost a sigh. "Saraltr was afraid you'd run away."

"I've thought of that. But where could I go? My demon lives inside. I can't run away from him."

Sharlyn blinked away tears with nictitating membranes. "I suppose not. If only I could take you with me to the subsea colonies."

"Are you going back?"

"I was only waiting for you. *She* tired of them. I have only visited nereids briefly. But *I* don't find them dull. I thought you would like them, and might want to come."

"You mean become a nereid? Hybridization?"

"Just a thought."

Luellan was quiet for a moment, thinking. Then he spoke softly: "I hadn't thought of that. Would hybridization overcome progeria? Did any of the other children become hybrids?"

"Not that I can remember. Normally hybridization is not attempted before adulthood. The process would arrest development. It might be possible. Edbryn would know. He's the best genosurgeon in Nyssa."

Luellan felt his heart racing. But he dared not hope. Still, it might be possible. And the environments opened by hybridization were almost unlimited. He could become a whisperbird and soar in the air. Nereids lived comfortably beneath the sea. There were a score of new races that had been adapted to colonize habitable planets and moons. Once Sharlyn had taken Luellan to visit Port of Nyssa beneath the icesea. He had marveled at the myriad of creatures walking about: lizards from Mars, winged batmen from Ganymede; elves from the crystal forests of Titan; mining gnomes from the asteroids; icemen from Pluto; chameleons who could change their shapes at will to adapt to a variety of environments; bald sailors with ebony skin and eyes blue as deep space; and one catlike creature, with the black skin, nictitating membranes, and shining monomer sweat of a sailor, but also with bat ears, a long prehensile tail, blue electric glow from each palm, and long fingers with hollow claws. When Luellan asked what the creatures were, Sharlyn had replied in a whisper—chimerae. Later he learned they had been hybridized during the space wars to resuscitate wounded soldiers. Each finger produced a different neuropeptide hormone that could be injected by their claws. Their salivary glands produced endolepsin. The touch of their tongues would produce pleasant euthanasia.

The possibilities of hybridization were endless. And he had nothing to lose. His only alternative was rapid aging and death. Or something worse. He remembered Lady Blue.

"What is it like to be with Lady Blue?" he asked.

"They say it's very pleasant. Just like sleeping. Only slower. A dream can last for decades. An endless fugue of pleasant reverie."

Luellan saw again his frost-giant, heard him roar.

"How can I talk to Edbryn?" he asked.

"He'll be at Saraltr's waking tomorrow."

Then there would be time. He could delay Petraltr until he had talked to Edbryn and found out if hybridization was possible and if it would prevent progeria. But something else still bothered him. "Why must Saraltr's integration come now? Why can't she wait for me?"

Sharlyn did not answer. She kissed his cheek. He could feel her sharp canine teeth beneath her lips. Then she lay back. He heard her singing. He knew the song.

"Why?" he asked again.

"It's in the song," she answered. "Listen to the song. Lady Blue knows why."

Luellan went back to sleep with the ballad running through his mind.

He woke in the half-light of dawn. Stars were fading through persplex. Sharlyn was gone. He wondered what had wakened him so early. He could remember no other nightmares. Something else had. He listened. There was soft singing. He left bed and crept quietly down the hall. Yes, now he could hear singing plainly. Someone else sang the ballad. Always the same song. Did it have meaning for all? But a different singer. Who this time?

He went down stairs to a balcony and peered onto the solarium. Saraltr sat in her bonsai. She was singing to herself. Her hands rested on gnarled bark. Singing stones adorned her fingers. Their light danced crazily across her body, casting bizarre shadows, and reflected from the waxy leaves of the trees. For the first time he noticed the tremor in her fingers that caused her rings to quiver. Luellan wanted to go to her, to tell her he understood and forgave her. But he stayed where he was and only listened to her sing, instead. The morning air was cold.

7

All morning, guests had been arriving for Saraltr's wake. They came dressed in party finery: gossamer capes of spider-silk, sheer scarves tied around arms or legs or waists, living furs clinging to shoulders, but mostly bare skin with animated tattoos engaged in erotic postures. Fingers, toes, ears, and noses were adorned with sonic jewelry. The faint singing of hundreds of stones blended with the laughter of many voices and mingled into a cacaphony of sound. Hybrids were scattered among the crowd: whisperbirds perched in bonsai, wolfmen paced nervously, sphinx brushed against bare legs and purred, and a pair of bears rolled somersaults. Centaurs cavorted with each other on the lawn outside.

Petraltr and Saraltr greeted each guest as they arrived; embracing, kissing, caressing, then directing them to tables laden with food and drink. Servmech wandered among the guests with trays balanced on their shoulders. The fragrance of mnemone drifted in the air. Teeth shone with the colors of peptide.

Luellan sat with Sharlyn on a balcony above the foyer, watching the guests arrive. He was waiting for Edbryn. There was something he wanted to ask him.

In the middle of the room beyond, on a raised dais, was Saraltr's integration coffin. It was lined with white satin. Its walls were transparent. A gleaming helmet rested at one end. Later, a body would lie upon the cushions. The helmet would be placed over her head. The coffin would fill with DMSO. Microfilaments would sprout from the helmet's lining, pierce her skull, and infiltrate brain tissue. Transducers in the helmet were connected to a neurocrystal that had been carefully grown over the past five years. The crystal would be transcribed with the electrochemical gestalt that defined her persona. Her self-awareness, her sense of "I," would be transferred from human brain to crystalline synthecortex, to become thought without feeling. She would become part of the vast myriad of minds comprising mind-mech, leaving behind the distractions of emotion, existing in the ascetic limbo of rational contemplation, untroubled by fear or worry, devoid of anger or pain, lacking as well joy and pleasure.

Luellan could think of her integration in the abstract, but when he put Saraltr's face on the form in the coffin, a strange hurt swelled in his mind. But he thought he understood why her wake must be now.

Sharlyn touched his shoulder. She beckoned to the door with a clawed finger. Luellan looked, hoping it was Edbryn. But instead she pointed to two sailors just arriving. Such splendid creatures they were: a man and a woman, both tall and lithe, almost naked, skin black as oiled teak, wearing only capes of soft polymer. Their skulls were bald and glistened with contact jelly. Their scalps stretched taut over a network of vitalium wire embedded beneath skin, giving it the textured appearance of brain coral. Nictitating membranes flipped occasionally across their eyes. Ears and nostrils could be closed with sphincters.

"Who are they?" Luellan asked. He shook his hair about his shoulders.

"Old friends," said Sharlyn. "Very old friends who went to space a long time ago. This is their first time back to earth for many years."

"How wonderful they appear." Luellan imagined himself looking as they did. He was pleased with the image. He hoped Edbryn would arrive soon. "Did they know Saraltr?" he asked.

The nereid nodded. "They come back for her wake. Very old friends indeed. Come, you must meet them." She took the boy by his hand and led him down the stairs.

"Laura, Damiel." The sailors turned; their eyes were sapphire blue. They embraced Sharlyn, each kissing her lips in turn.

"So," Damiel said in a voice close to a whisper, "you've already given up the life beneath the sea." As an aside to Luellan: "We underwent hybridization at the same time, those many years ago. Ennui struck us at the same time. Laura and I became gravsailors, while Sharlyn chose instead to become a sea-manimal." Then he paused and looked deep into the nereid's eyes. "But wait, this is not the Sharlyn I knew. Don't tell me . . ."

Sharlyn glanced to the glass coffin. Damiel understood at once.

"How long ago?" he asked.

"Twenty years. Even *she* grew bored cruising the antarctic reefs. Space must be better. But *I* do remember you. Such good friends you were with *her*. I hope you will like *me* as well. Yes," she said wistfully, "space must be better."

"A little, anyway. And this must be Luellan." He touched the boy's shoulder lightly. "Have you been to space yet?"

"No," said Luellan, "not yet." Wondering if there would be time. Surely the sailor knew what fate he faced. Unless Edbryn could help. He saw himself as a sailor again. Yes, hybridization was his only chance. It had to work. "But someday soon I would like to go to space," he added.

"Good. You'll listen to my stories. Everyone else will find them quite dull and think of me as an old bore. Their interest has been jaded by excessive decadence. But I'll wager I can interest a youngster like you. When I'm through I'll bet you hop the next sailship out." He put his arm around Luellan's shoulders and led him aside. They found cushions and seated themselves. Damiel selected two tall tumblers from a passing tray, drained one with one long draw, and sipped on the other as he began telling space tales. Laura and Sharlyn sat near, with Laura resting her hand on the nereid's furred leg. There was a strange resemblance between the two women. Sharlyn had sleek grey fur covering her body, with hair of the same length on her head, vestigial ears, eyes blurred behind a nictitating membrane. Laura had a sailor's baldness with flat ears molded to fit inside a navigation helmet. She too had nictitating membranes that served as radiation filters to protect her eyes from fierce sunlight. They were dilated in the comparative dimness of earth. Vaguely, he remembered cetacean DNA had been used in part to transform sailors.

Luellan became entranced by Damiel's low voice as he told stories of the outer moons. He imagined swift trigee racers with gravsails furled, riding the currents of gravity, crewed by splendid creatures able to endure the fierce radiation and cold vacuum of deep space. And he saw even Damiel's eyes soften when he told of the lost lamia and the songs they sang that came to sailors in their dreams, to tempt ships to blunder beyond the trans-Pluto life barrier.

"Have you been so tempted, Damiel?" Luellan asked.

The sailor's face stiffened. His visual filters contracted to opaqueness, then dilated. "Once, just once I heard their song waking, and only briefly, or I would not now be here. For they say a sailor hears his own voice singing as a lamia, his own thoughts caught up in the time warp of the barrier. For some time I was wont to sit and ponder about things that might have been. But Firiel brought me back to sanity."

"Firiel? Who is she?"

"A chimera. It is said only she truly understands lamia. Her lover is one of them. He has tormented her for years. Now she is totally mad. But with madness, has come understanding. She uses her neuropeptides to bring reason back to a sailor driven mad by lamia. The irony is that she cannot help herself."

Luellan wanted to listen to him more, but they were interrupted by Saraltr coming to stand before them. Damiel rose to embrace her. She released him slowly.

"It's been a long time," he said.

Saraltr nodded. "I'm glad you could come. One never knows if messages reach you sailors."

Luellan sensed something more than words was being spoken between them. But then they had known each other some time ago.

He looked around for Edbryn. He would not have much time now. He had spent more time than he had realized listening to Damiel. But he did not see the genosurgeon. He was distracted by a commotion across the room. Someone was shouting. Some of the other guests were trying to restrain him.

Bodies surged forward. A man lunged from the crowd. It was Dandarl, the man who had visited his parents earlier. There was something wrong with his face. Spittle drooled from his mouth. His features were held lax.

Dandarl ran to the crystal coffin and kneeled before it. He ran his hands over the glass, then pressed his face into its side, smearing saliva with his lips and tongue. Then he crawled inside and lay upon its satin cushions.

The guests were held immobile by astonishment.

Then Saraltr screamed, guessing what Dandarl would attempt. She ran toward the coffin. Dandarl reached for the integration helmet and attempted to place it on his head. Saraltr grasped it also and tugged against him, pulling it from his hands.

Dandarl sat up in the coffin. His face was flaccid. He looked around with puzzled eyes, then saw Saraltr clutching the integration helmet. He began to sob. Then he flailed his hands against his face. Blood welled from both nostrils.

Luellan looked from Dandarl to Saraltr.

He understood. His guess had been correct.

He knew why her integration had to occur now, why she could not wait for him. If she waited, she would become like Dandarl had become. She was afraid of that more than anything. He could see fear contorting her features.

And he saw the same expression mirrored on every face in the room. They all shared her fear. They would all eventually become like Dandarl. Only integration could salvage intellect. Lady Blue could only preserve it.

Suddenly it seemed too hot. The guests seemed too close. He hungered for fresh air.

Luellan turned and ran, pushing past people still crowded in the doorway.

There was someplace he still had to find again.

8

Outside the sun was declining. The air held the coolness of dusk. Anian came to his whistle immediately, for once not being playfully coy. It almost seemed as if she had been waiting for him. He grabbed a handful of mane, pulled himself astride her back, and kicked her gently in the flanks. She reared briefly, then cantered across the lawn toward the orchards beyond.

Luellan lay forward, placed his cheek against her sturdy neck, and closed his eyes. Images crowded into his sensorium: a frost-giant bellowed rage; aged children were imprisoned within clear ice; the empty eyes of Saraltr stared from her crystal coffin; and superimposed on each was a transparent face, a face with cyanotic skin, sapphire teeth, framed with hair that shone like spun tourmaline, crystalline eyes. *Lady Blue, with eyes of ice.* Sharlyn said it was in the song. He let the words run through his mind. Yes, it was all there. Understanding hurt.

Luellan opened his eyes to drive away disturbing images. It was almost dark. Anian cantered through dark forest. Somewhere far above a whisperbird called. Its raspy voice broke the quiet like a wine glass shattering in resonance. Ahead, starlight flashed white.

Anian stopped abruptly before permasteel gates. Muscles twitched beneath her skin.

Beyond lay the Alabaster Fortress.

Luellan jumped from the centaur's back. His feet sank deep into soft loam. He pushed the gates open. They swung smoothly on their hinges. He walked quietly toward the building. Sweat formed on his palms. Yet the building was dark and still. Its windows shone with the last of the sunset. Behind, the centaur grazed nervously.

Finally he stood before great bronze doors. He listened carefully. All was quiet. He reached out cautiously and touched the door, then jerked his hand back quickly. But there was nothing to be alarmed about. No noise startled him. He felt silly. Any demon was within him. Luellan again touched the door. Its metal was cool. He pressed a stud in its center. The doors opened easily, with a faint hum of machinery.

He stood poised on the threshold, ready to flee back to Anian. His heart pounded in his chest. His mouth was dry. But it was quiet within the building. There was no sound of movement inside. Nothing to cause alarm. He took a step forward and then paused. Still quiet. Another step, another pause. He stood inside. The air smelled stale and was a little acrid with ozone. It was dark. But the quiet persisted. He felt along the wall. The marble was smooth. He found a stud; his finger poised over it. Stillness remained. No movement. He pressed the stud. His legs were flexed, ready to carry him away.

Light sprang forth from panels in the ceiling, flooding the interior with harsh illumination. Brilliance blurred his vision. There was no movement. As his eyes adjusted to the glare, Luellan saw a central dais within one large room. Shelving lined the walls all the way to the high ceiling, five stories above. Clear cylinders were stacked upon the shelving. There were thousands of the cylinders. He knew what they held.

He walked to the dais. A control console was built into its side. Luellan pressed the red activator stud. A liquid crystal display glowed with luminescence. He randomly pressed studs, filling the display with numerals. A light flashed green. Machinery whined faintly. Far above, a cylinder moved along quiet conveyors.

Luellan climbed to the top of the dais and waited. A cylinder extruded through an orifice. Green light stopped flashing from the display panel. He stared for a long time into crystalline walls.

The cylinder was a sarcophagus. A body lay within, suspended face down in red viscous liquid. The body rotated about its axis, turning supine. Convex walls magnified the image beyond life-size. Luellan waited for it to complete its turning. A plaque was attached to the end of the sarcophagus, with lettering etched into satin stainless steel. The same number that had glowed on the display appeared on the plaque. Below the number was a name: Carode Geogrs, Pine Bluffs, Wyoming. A.D. 1998.

As the face appeared he realized he had been holding his breath. He let it out in a deep sigh. She had been beautiful. *Was beautiful,* he corrected the thought, *would still be beautiful, would always be the same.* And so young. The body held within the sarcophagus was that of a girl barely beyond pubescence, still glowing with adolescence. Her breasts were small and firm, lagging in growth behind their nipples. She had an awkward angularity with long limbs yet to be padded with female adipose. Her face still held innocence in its features, even though they were now held in rigid immobility. Her head was bald, giving her a nun's vulnerability. *So lovely . . .*

A hand touched his shoulder. He turned. A startled cry choked in his throat. His legs melted with weakness.

"Do you like her? Do you admire my little child?"

Luellan could not answer. A naked woman stood beside him, her hand on his shoulder. Her skin was blue, her eyes flawed turquoise. She too was bald. No, not bald, for stubble grew from her scalp, like bluegrass sprouting from seed. Luellan's knees were shaking. His voice was still a lump in his throat. The face was the one he had glimpsed in the window. She was Lady Blue.

"Do you know her?" Lady Blue spoke again. Her voice sounded hollow. "So pretty. But then they are all so pretty. And all are mine." Some quality to her voice seemed familiar. "Have you come for a little visit? We get so few visitors now. Only that man a few days ago. We had such a lovely visit. But he hasn't been back since. No one comes to talk to my pretties. No one comes to talk to me." The words were slurred. Her face sagged in laxity. He noticed her hand still rested on his shoulder. There was a tremor in her fingers. He had guessed the truth. Such a terrible secret they had kept from him.

"She won't harm you." Luellan turned to look to the doorway. Petraltr stood there. "Don't be afraid of her," he said, "she's quite harmless." He came forward.

Lady Blue turned, letting her hand fall from Luellan's shoulder. "Another visitor? Come in, come in."

Lady of death, refuses to die.

"Have you come to see my lovelies?" she asked Petraltr. "I was once one of them, too. You see, once I was going to die. But I fooled him. I let them freeze me away until a cure was found. And one was found. I was cured. I even took a lover." She paused. Her eyes brimmed with tears. "I do miss him. He was such a good man." She looked from Petraltr to Luellan. "He got old and died. But I didn't. Get old, I mean. Sometimes I think I died a long time ago."

Petraltr walked to the console. He touched his fingers to the panel. The sarcophagus sank into the dais.

"Goodbye, Carode," Luellan whispered, "will I ever see you again?"

Lady of night, who lived twice.

An empty sarcophagus took the place of the previous one. Lady Blue stared at it blankly. Petraltr climbed to the top of the dais. He took her hand and kissed it. "My Lady," he said, "I am sorry your sleep has been disturbed. Your dreams have been rudely interrupted."

"Lady," she repeated in wonder. "Did they used to call me such?" She brought her hand to her forehead. "Why, yes, I believe they did. But why?"

Lady of pain, too old to cry.

"You must be tired," Petraltr said. "You need a little nap."

"Why, yes, I am tired. If only I could sleep, get a little rest. A nap would do nicely. The little dears can be quite tiring. And I was having such a lovely dream. Do you suppose my dream will continue?"

"Of course it will." Petraltr lead her to the empty sarcophagus. He touched its side. Invisible seams cracked and it split into halves. "Here we are, m'lady. Time for a little nap." He helped her climb into one of the half-cylinders. "Sweet dreams," he crooned.

Lady Blue, with eyes of ice.

She lay supine and closed her eyes. Another touch by Petraltr and the sarcophagus closed. Gas filled the inside, forming a filigree of frost on the woman, then fogged the walls. Red fog coalesced and dripped from the inside surfaces, to melt the frost from the woman.

Petraltr looked at Luellan. "Liquid helium," he said, gesturing toward the sarcophagus. "Held near absolute zero."

"Why was she awake?"

"Dandarl must have wakened her. I doubt if he realized what he was doing." Petraltr looked away. "A long time ago this place was used to preserve people with incurable diseases. They were held in suspended animation to await the cure for their diseases. Only sometimes the cures were worse than the ailments. Have you guessed what we tried to keep hidden?" Liquid helium continued to condense and drip.

"I think so. Most of it." He felt cold inside.

"You know the ballad. The story is all there. Lady Blue had a rare condition called hereditary carcinomatosis. Every tissue in her body would eventually turn malignant. But she chose cryogenic sleep to await a cure. And cured she was. The ancients finally developed effective antineoplastic drugs. She was foolish enough to consent to their treatment. For she was young and by then in love and did not want to die. And she didn't. The drugs worked. As long as she took them, she did not develop cancer. Then something strange and wonderful happened; she did not age. While her lover grew old and senile, she stayed youthful and vigorous. When he died an old man, she was as young as when she married him. The genosurgeons studied her genes. It was found the genes that caused cancer were linked to repressor genes that blocked normal cellular senescence. The normal program coded in the DNA of each cell called for an inexorable pattern of growth, maturity, aging, then death. With Lady Blue's genes the program could be locked in the mature phase, circumventing both aging and death. The genes causing malignancy were excised from the DNA strand. The resultant piece of DNA was made into a miniature nucleus called a plasmid. A virus could be used to inject this plasmid into other cells. Great quantities of Lady Blue's cells were grown in tissue culture and their DNA harvested. The ova used to produce the first and second recombinant generations were given the little piece of DNA derived from Lady Blue. She is mother to us all. We are immortal because of her. Only death by accident occurs." He laughed hollowly.

"What went wrong?" Luellan asked, and remembered: *reason faded, skin blued.*

"Look at her." Petraltr rested his hand on the sarcophagus. Liquid helium had begun to climb the walls of the cylinder. "She is called Lady Blue because of a defect in collagen synthesis. Collagen is a glycoprotein fiber used in connective tissue. Her collagen fibers take up copper very slowly, which gives her connective tissue a blue color. In a normal life-span, it would not even be noticed. But Lady Blue has lived for over a thousand years. She became more and more blue as time passed."

"What is the connection?" But he knew: *Youth's a mask of fragile disguise, hiding life not renewed.*

"No, the connection was not obvious. No one guessed in time. The gene that caused abnormal copper accumulation was also linked to the antiagathic gene. No one knew of this linkage because no one knew this gene existed. So it was not excised from the plasmid DNA. It was inadvertently included on the DNA strand. But its effects were partly blocked."

"So no one turned blue."

"Exactly. The effects were not apparent. But copper was also taken up by the brain. The slow accumulation resulted in progressive dementia. You have listened to her. Do you think she started out as a half-wit?"

"And everyone has that gene now. Verdigris is growing in everyone's brain. So everyone will . . ." He stopped, remembering Saraltr's eyes.

"Hybridization only delays its expression. Integration to mindmech is the only escape." Petraltr laughed. "The only escape," he said again.

Lady Blue's sarcophagus was filled with liquid helium. Her eyes had opened. Ice had shattered them into blue shards.

Petraltr went to the console and changed the settings. Lady Blue disappeared into the dais. "There's still one more explanation, one more thing you must see." Another cryocoffin rose.

Luellan knew who would be inside.

Lorriel was almost the same as he remembered her, as when he had seen her last. Only her hair was gone, shaved off so it would not shatter when it froze and clog the cryogenic mechanism. Her face was still wrinkled. Her eyes were still opaque with cataracts. Her fingers were crooked with arthritic deformity. "Are all the third generation here?" he asked.

"Of course. They're all here. All but you."

"What happened to us? What went wrong with our generation?"

"Your parents were too late. For youth *was* a mask. We were not young. We had waited too long. Our germ cells had already exceeded

Hayflick's limit. Our gametes are defective. Their union produces defective offspring. We were too late for hybrid vigor to occur. You age at an accelerated rate. Your bodies can't stand the stress of puberty. They would have died before adolescence was over. So would you." Petraltr looked carefully at Luellan. "But they didn't die. Nor will you."

"They didn't die because they're frozen away. Waiting for what? Can there be a cure?" He thought of Edbryn, of ebony sailors. He had not had a chance to talk to him.

Petraltr shrugged. "No, not for you. No cure." His hands played over the console. Lorriel disappeared. An empty cryocoffin replaced hers. "We didn't tell you where Lorriel was because we . . ." he stopped to clear his throat.

"Because?" But he knew.

"Lorriel didn't want to come here. There was a little unpleasantness when we brought her here. But Saraltr couldn't stand to see Lorriel die. She doesn't want you to die either. I'm afraid we're not used to seeing death anymore. The concept bothers our sensibilities." He touched the sarcophagus. It broke into halves. Vapor misted within.

"Wait!" Luellan said. His bones ached with cold. "Maybe the progeria can be overcome." He thought with furious speed, using memories derived from learning crystals. It might work. Only Edbryn would know for certain. His speech held desperate pressure: "Maybe the medmech could not devise a cure. But could the progeria be overcome by hybridization? Couldn't hybrid vigor be obtained that way? Wouldn't the infusion of xenogenes correct my defective ones? Edbryn would know. Let's find out from him. What is there to lose. Only a little time."

Petraltr had not been listening. He was lost to his own musings. "Time. 'Ah, there's the rub.' There's no time left, Lue. Saraltr must be integrated today. I wish there was enough time." He held his hands out. "See for yourself. There's no time left at all." His fingers had a fine tremor in them. "It won't hurt. You'll go to sleep . . . for a long time. You'll have all the time in the world, then. Your dreams will last forever." He gestured to the waiting cryocoffin.

Luellan stared at it. Helium sublimated to gas. Water vapor from the air frosted into snow. He saw a frost-giant smiling through steel whiskers, waiting to blow his icy breath. There had to be another way. He had to take the chance there was.

He turned and ran.

"Lue, come back!" Petraltr shouted. "It's better this way. I promised your mother."

Luellan ran out the door. He did not look back. He ran past steel gates. Anian waited. He leaped on her back, kicking her into a gallop.

They ran along the beach. Anian's hooves threw sand high in the air. Luellan leaned over the centaur's neck. Cool wind blew against his face. There was a tang of salt in the air.

Above, unseen in darkness, a whisperbird sounded its hunting cry.

Luellan nudged Anian's side. She veered to the right, away from the beach, and ran on to the ice without breaking stride. Her steel-shod hooves clattered against the frozen surface. Again the cry from above, sounding louder.

The space needle was far ahead. A sailship catapulted upward. Ice shuddered as compressed force dissipated along the needle into the sea. Heat of expansion was drawn from the water. A crack shot through the ice beneath them. Anian's sure hooves did not falter. Luellan thought of the sailors in the gravship. They were going to the outer moons. Adventure was to be found out there. He saw himself in the ship. He lay in clear gel in an acceleration chamber. Starlight gleamed from skin dark as obsidian. A navhelmet was on his head. Lines of gravity swirled through his mind. Monomer sails were like his own hands catching gravity.

As the sailship left atmosphere, its gravsails unfolded and it accelerated along the lines of force. Sunlight from the far side of earth reflected from monomer sails. A new star blazed briefly, then receded and winked out. Luellan closed his eyes, then lay his head on Anian's neck. He wished desperately he was leaving with the sailship. A pleasant fantasy built in his mind: Wings whistled near; great clawed toes rested on his shoulders, but did not hurt; carefully they closed on the fabric of his cape, not even scratching his skin; her wings unfolded and beat against air; he was lifted from the centaur's back; the whisperbird carried him upward into the cold night sky, chasing a fading star.

Before the fantasy faded, a decision had been made.

9

Edbryn, Lord of Nyssa, a member of the Council of the Seventeen, foremost genosurgeon, gazed to the west, as though in need of arranging his thoughts. He stared for a long time through the thick persplex dome of his penthouse office, atop Nyssa's tallest tower. His eyes and hair were the same shade of distinguished grey. He was a tall man, with long, supple fingers. Edbryn looked twenty years older than his actual physiologic age. But appearances were important to a genosurgeon—they were his prime commodity. Luellan wondered how much Edbryn's own visage had to be cosmetically altered to achieve its look of confident dignity. Probably a considerable amount, he decided.

Luellan waited nervously for Edbryn to speak. His palms were sweaty. He felt a tightness in his belly. What the genosurgeon said was of life and death importance to Luellan, literally. Because he had already decided that under no circumstances would he sleep with Lady Blue.

It had been over a week since he and Petraltr had gone to Edbryn with his question. Edbryn had said the idea would require study. He could not say how long it would take. The waiting had been terrible for Luellan. He had been summoned only that morning for this appointment.

Of course, things did happen while he was waiting.

Petraltr had undergone his integration, joining Saraltr in the joyless existence of mindmech. Luellan had gone to live with Lord Gordon, a neighbor and one of his parents' closest friends, while awaiting word from Edbryn.

Gordon now sat beside Luellan. He had bushy red eyebrows and a shock of unruly auburn hair. His eyes were green and held mirth in them. He had been busy making discreet phone calls for the past few days. There was an air of barely restrained secrecy about him that made Luellan uneasy. He knew something was about. But he dared not hope too much.

Edbryn finally turned from the transparent wall. He was smiling. "How shall I begin," he said. "A long time ago a type of joke began— I've got some good news and some bad news. Maybe that's what I should say. I've certainly got both kinds for you. A most interesting proposal you brought me, young man. Most interesting indeed. Rattled a few brains around here. A shame no one thought of it earlier."

Luellan felt as though his heart was racing. "Then will it work?" He tried to remain calm.

"Maybe. There's a reasonable chance, anyway. A certain risk, too, of course. There always is."

Luellan realized he had been holding his breath. He released it slowly. Gordon cuffed him on the shoulder. His grin was wider than Luellan's.

Edbryn continued: "We still don't know exactly what defect causes the progeria. Something produced by Hayflick's phenomenon, certainly. But we could find nothing specific to correct. It never occurred to us to try nonspecific measures. Medmech are somewhat unimaginative, I'm afraid. And I guess the rest of us have forgotten how to be physicians, it's been so long since there was any need for us. Anyway, I ramble. Yes, hybridization might work. The hybrid vigor produced by the melding of xenogenes might prevent accelerated aging from occurring." He looked to the mountains, blue with haze. "Of course there's a hooker."

"There always is." Luellan laughed. It would work, he told himself.

"Complete hybridization would arrest your normal development. You would not complete puberty. You would always be a child."

"I could take that, I suppose. That's not so bad."

"You may not have to. Complete hybridization may not be necessary. Partial transformation should be just as effective in promoting hybrid vigor. We can selectively transform only tissues that have already matured, allowing the others to develop normally."

"Which tissues? What kind of hybrid must I become?" Luellan thought of crisp lines of gravity, sunlight gleaming from billowed monomer.

"Unfortunately we are somewhat limited there. Your nervous system is the only tissue in your body that's fully developed now. But Lord Gordon tells me you want to be a sailor."

Luellan nodded, seeing again the faces of Laura and Damiel. Ebony skin shone. Occular membranes glistened silver. "How would that be possible?" he asked. "They have had every tissue modified."

Edbryn laughed. "Only because sailors are so vain. Most of their modifications, though protective to a degree, are really unnecessary. The only vital changes are to augment cerebellum and motor cortex, expanding both three-space equilibrium and kinesthetic capability. And the implantation of e-wires, of course, but that's simple cybersurgery. The modification of the nervous system with avian, chiropteran, and cetacean DNA is the most important part. Especially for you. Because there should be enough hybrid vigor in those genes to block your progeria." He paused, smiling. "What do you say? Want to give it a try?"

Luellan remembered steel whiskers and breath colder than ice. He shivered. The ballad of Lady Blue filled his head. He pushed away the song. "When can I start?" he asked.

"Right now." Edbryn led Luellan across the office. They stepped into a gravshaft, drifted down several floors, then exited into a brightly lit genosurgery theater. Medmech stood discreetly behind a permasteel tank brimming with crimson liquid media.

Edbryn seated Luellan in a cushioned chair. A medmech padded over and stood before them, holding a tray in his hands. A clear ampul rested on the tray. Luellan picked it up and held it in front of him.

"A simple hypnotic," Edbryn said. "Though the medium is well oxygenated, most people object to breathing liquid. They find it more pleasant to be asleep when immersed."

"How long will it take?"

Edbryn shrugged. "That varies. Normally a few weeks. For total transformation. The process is much like embryogenesis. The more modification required, the longer time in broth. Maybe a little less time for you." He paused. "No, on second thought, I imagine it will take just as long. For other reasons." He smiled secretly.

Luellan looked around. "What happened to Gordon?" he asked. He remembered then that Gordon had not followed them from Edbryn's office.

"He'll be waiting for you when you awaken." Again the secret smile. "You know how to use the ampul?"

Luellan nodded. But still he paused. Uncertainty made him wait. He had the irrational fear he was being tricked. What if this was all an elaborate ruse? Maybe when he was asleep they would take him to Lady Blue. He saw blue lips laugh, with fear held in fractured sapphire eyes. He had no choice. He had to trust Edbryn. There was something worse than death, but he had to take that chance.

Luellan snapped open the ampul and inhaled its sweet vapor deep into his lungs. The edges of consciousness narrowed. Darkness drifted over him.

When he woke, sunlight was sparkling from the leaves of bonsai. Water splashed from a fountain. Luellan was home, in the solarium. He was sitting in a fungoid lounge chair. He wondered if he had dreamed the meeting with Edbryn. He looked at his hands. They were no different. The finger pads did not have the tree-frog suction cups that sailors' did. The rest of his body seemed unchanged as well. He felt his head. It was bald. Ridges could be felt beneath the skin, where vitalium wires were coiled.

No, not dreaming. No dream had implanted e-wires beneath his scalp. He felt strange—as though his eyes were closed, or his ears were plugged, or his fingers were numb, although they were not. Something was missing. He needed to see more, hear more, feel more.

He got up. Somehow, it felt as though two arms and two legs were not enough. There should be more. He seemed to be in darkness. Everything seemed dim.

He heard a familiar laugh. A shape moved out of the foliage of bonsai. A sailor walked over to stand beside him. His skin gleamed like oiled teak. There was something familiar about him. Nictitating membranes blinked over dark eyes beneath bushy red eyebrows.

"Gordon! You too?" Incredulously: "But how? Why?"

"You mean, of course. I couldn't let you go to space alone. Petraltr appointed me your guardian. I take his trust seriously. Besides, it'll be fun. I was getting tired of old earth."

Luellan looked at his hands. "Something's wrong. Hybridization must not have worked for me. Why do I feel so empty? What's wrong with me?"

"Nothing. Nothing at all is wrong. Your brain wants more imput and output, that's all. It's designed now for more efferents and afferents than it has available. A navhelmet will provide those. You'll feel fine as soon as you become a cyborg with a sailship."

Luellan shook his head. "When can we go? I'm getting claustrophobia."

"Anytime you like. Everything has been arranged. I even talked Nyssa's last naval architect into building a trigee racer for us. Vicsn says he's surpassed even himself with it. We'll see soon enough."

"Good. Let's go. My brain itches."

"Don't you even want to say goodbye?" another familiar voice asked. Sharlyn lay in a bonsai, his mother's former tree. Her body molded perfectly into the sculpted branch. "Is it that important to go?" Her eyes brimmed with tears. She blinked them away.

Luellan went to her and held her tight. "Yes," he said. "It is that important." But he knew she would never understand.

He spent one last night with Sharlyn. They talked until it was almost light. No promises had to be broken; none had been made. They were each lost to their own thoughts as their bodies moved toward love. Later, as he lay beneath the lightening dome with sweat cooling on his skin, Luellan knew that he had made the right choice, the only possible one. For he discovered that puberty had finally occurred as he lay in genosurgical broth. He knew he would not have wanted to miss the delights it brought.

He touched her shoulder. Sharlyn stirred. He nuzzled into her soft fur. He would miss her. But he had no choice.

10

Port of Nyssa bustled with activity: sailors sauntered casually about as they waited for their berths to depart; newly arrived off-worlders walked clumsily as they adjusted to one G; departing tourists bade friends goodbye; baggage moved rapidly along conveyors; peddlers hawked their wares—mnemone, peptide, dream-dust. Every five minutes there would be a shudder as a gravship was catapulted up the space needle into orbit.

Luellan and Gordon had just arrived from Nyssa a few minutes earlier. While being whisked along at a hundred km/h in the subsea evacuated tube, they had watched the panorama of the sea floor through its transparent walls. Clusters of glowing domes perched along the rim of a deep trench. Kelp pastures with schools of grazing tuna feeding on krill spread along the flats. Nereid herders sometimes looked up and waved. Sharlyn had gone to live in the nereid colony beneath the icesea. Luellan swam with her until the shallows had dropped off into waters too deep for him. Before she left, she pressed her face into the oxygen bubble that surrounded his head, and kissed him quickly on the lips. He hoped she would find the same happiness that awaited him in space.

A sailor approached them, crossing the crowded lobby. She and Gordon embraced, then she turned to face Luellan, smiling.

"You've met Laura, haven't you Lue?" Gordon asked.

Luellan nodded. "It seems like a long time ago," he said.

"She's agreed to come with us and teach us how to sail a gravship."

"Mostly they sail themselves," Laura said, laughing. "Fine technique is only important when racing."

"We intend to do a little of that, don't we Lue?" Gordon laughed too.

Luellan could not keep from grinning. *It would work.* He laughed out loud. *It would work,* he told himself again. This time he believed himself.

They had boarded their gravship. Gordon had named her *Wyvern,* saying she looked like a winged creature of night.

They lay within acceleration chambers, immersed in clear gelatin. Each wore a navhelmet. The thoughts of Laura and Gordon were soft in Luellan's mind.

Wyvern moved along a conveyor. Soon it would be her turn to be thrown into space. An indicator in the ship's chart in each sailor's mind beeped down the time remaining before launch.

Luellan let his mind wander. There would be nothing to do until they were in orbit. He saw Anian frolicking about her pasture, with Alelis drifting in the high air currents. They had found their peace. Now it was his turn. Images crowded beneath consciousness. He let them rise. He was not afraid.

A wolf-pack hunts, drifting across the icesea like silent ghosts. Their eyes are bright with moonlight.

He saw again the Alabaster Fortress. Lorriel would always be waiting, sleeping with Lady Blue. Her dreams would be endless, last forever. If only they were pleasant.

Heavy footfalls come near.

Wyvern moved slowly along the conveyor. It was almost time. They were next to be launched. His wait was almost over.

A roar splits frozen air.

Luellan sang again the ballad of Lady Blue. The words held no fear for him now, only a sadness that lingered briefly. He would have died if need be. That was enough. No more could be asked.

Icy breath whistles near.

A gong sounded in his mind. *Wyvern* was nudged into position within the launch chamber of the gravshute. Seconds counted down, then were gone.

Icicle fingers click together close behind.

Compressed force expanded beneath *Wyvern,* accelerating her up the space needle. Luellan barely felt the Gs. They were no more than a comfortable pressure, pushing away the last of dark dreams.

Bright stars waited beyond the mirror of sky.

Lost behind is the frost-giant's futile roar.

That They Be Saved

BY
AL SARRANTONIO

I pray to God that I might save the souls of these people.

We hover over a small clearing surrounded by gently swaying trees. I see a green world through the port. Our spaceship tamps down a circle of deep grass and comes to rest. There is no exhaust, no fire; long ago our race mastered gravity. We are dressed as peaceful gods, with soft beards and flowing hair.

The natives descend upon our ship and caress its smooth surface with their long and supple fingers. Their faces are filled with adoration and soft piety; they believe we are gods from heaven. I murmur a silent prayer that I may yet change Margus's mind and turn our unholy mission into one of salvation for these people.

Margus releases the hatch and we descend to the ground. We float down, using small devices clipped to our garments. There are crude paintings of these devices, our spaceships, and members of our race on the walls of the caves on this planet. We come to rest on a low, flat rock which is inscribed with symbols. The natives pray to us, their voices a sweet susurrus: Margus lifts his hands above them and the litany ceases.

"We come," says Margus, through a device at his lips which amplifies his weak voice to a stable roar, "from the heavens. We come again to you." He spreads his hands out before him, a mock blessing. The natives fall to their knees and kiss the earth.

"Rise," Margus intones, and the natives stand up. They are small people, with gentle features. They are like their forests, green and fragile. Margus will lie to them; will attempt, unless I can dissuade him, to carry out the terrible, unholy plan.

"Go now," he says, "and return tomorrow with your chieftains. The

god Arde and I will come forth at sunrise. You will receive our blessing, and a few will be chosen for the first sacred rite. Go now, and
sleep." He feigns another benediction.

The natives bow and retreat quietly into the forests.

Night is coming. Margus and I float gently up to the hatch and
enter the spaceship. We secure the opening and sit down on our cushions to rest.

Margus looks moodily at his charts and logs. I stare at him, but he
ignores me. I can stand it no longer and finally I speak.

"Margus," I say, heatedly, "do you still intend to go through with
this?"

He does not look up from his charts. "You know the answer to that
question," he says, flatly.

"Margus, we cannot carry this plan out. We have no right to do
such a thing; the mere existence of orders from the Council does not
justify it. And besides, the vote was not unanimous."

He ignores me.

"Margus—"

He slams his report log down and turns toward me. "The only nega-
tive votes," he says angrily, "were cast by the members of your crazy
religious minority. I can't believe so many Council members have been
duped into joining your cult. If the minority were not so strong at the
moment, you wouldn't be here, and you know it. The plan was passed
by the majority, and your people promised not to interfere." The
makeup and his soft beard—a comic mask, really, considering the way
he leads his life—cannot hide the hardness of his eyes.

"Margus, don't you realize what we will be doing to these people?
What of God's Law? What of the *Karadah?*"

"Screw the *Karadah,*" he says, and the tone of his voice causes me to
call on God's help to keep my anger within me; without God's strength
and the knowledge of what is truly right I'm afraid I would rise from
my seat and strike him. Our entire voyage has been like this, and now
our nerves have been rubbed raw. He reaches behind him and pulls
his bottle of liquor from his cubicle, uncaps it and throws his head
back, taking a large swallow. He spits on the floor of our cabin and
continues, in the same mocking tone. "Arde, you're a fool. You're all
fools. There hasn't been any organized religion on our planet for two
hundred years, and suddenly some sun-cooked lunatic digging in the
desert stumbles onto a stone tablet with a few scrawls on it—most
probably a hoax perpetrated by a practical joker or irresponsible non-
conformist—calls it the *Karadah,* and a third of the population cries

'God is with us!' and follows blindly. You people are ridiculous. We've been coming to this planet and others, doing what we're doing, for a hell of a long time, and there's no way a bunch of religious nuts are going to change that."

"We believe the *Karadah*, Margus. And it tells us we are God's chosen people. Is that so hard for you to understand?"

He is silent, a taunting smile on his lips.

"God's commandments—"

He has taken another drink and now he interrupts me. "God's commandments? Where is God, Arde? Where is your proof of this *Karadah's* authenticity?"

We have been over this many times, it is like arguing with a child. I say quietly, "If you have faith—"

"*Faith?*"

I am silent, nearly trembling with frustration at his stonelike atheism, his smugness, his unwillingness even to listen to my arguments. He takes a final drink, caps his bottle, and rises from the cushion.

"You want to see God, Arde?" He stands over me, leaning down, and his face is very ugly and red. He is not very drunk but there is warm alcohol on his breath. "*We* are God, Arde; you and I." He presses a finger into my chest. "On this planet, and others, we are gods; we make the laws and the commandments, and make these people do whatever we want. Tomorrow you'll see that, my friend; you'll see just what religion is good for. And they'll do just what we want, because we tell them to."

"I *have* to think about saving these people," I say, looking directly into his eyes.

He begins to laugh and then suddenly he raises his hand and brings it down across my face, hard. He steadies me, a hand on each shoulder, his thumbs pressing into my flesh. "I've told you," he says, the words coming slowly and sharply, a little drunkenly, "that you will not interfere with what we have to do. I told the Council that I would stand no interference, and your religious people agreed. I'm sick of your preaching, and sick to death of your religion. There's no possible way you could ever sway me over to your foolishness." He points to the floor, to the storage area below our feet where the apparatus is stored. "We have a job to do, and tomorrow we're going to begin doing it. That's the only reason we're here." His thumbs dig deeper into my shoulders, and his liquored breath is sickly sweet. "And that's all we're going to do, Arde."

He straightens, turns his back on me, and floats to the sleeping quarters. The lights dim.

I lie awake in my cushion, staring tight-lipped at the walls of the cabin and praying. I almost feel like crying. I will not let him do this. The Council's decision was wrong. A growing number of members have gained their faith and there was a long and bitter fight; but there were not enough votes to change the plan. I have tried in every way since the beginning of our mission to make Margus see what we must do, and now time is growing short. God's commandments, inscribed on the *Karadah*, preach restraint and patience with those who hate and persecute us, but they are also clear in commanding us to save souls for God. I begin to pray, and as I speak the words of the *Karadah*, softly, one at a time, a peace comes over me:

> *This does the Lord God command His chosen people,*
> *For they are born holy unto Him:*
> *That all men treat themselves as temples of God,*
> *And other men as themselves,*
> *And avoid corruption of flesh and mind*
> *And thus live in His love;*
> *And that this Word be spread by His people,*
> *Who are born in baptism unto Him,*
> *That others be baptised*
> *And thus brought unto Him and live in His love. . . .*

I pause, and an image of the baptism of the people of this wet, beautiful world comes to me, and a smile touches my lips and lingers there.

I finish my prayer, and lie for a moment in peace before reality rushes back at me. It pains me greatly to think of what we might do to the gentle beings of this planet if the plan as it is is carried out. I cannot take part in condemning them. I must save them.

Even if I must oppose Margus.

Sunlight filters through the port and settles on my eyes. It is dawn, and I have slept the night in my cushion. I hear the murmur of sweet voices outside the ship. The natives have come.

Margus has risen and prepares to open the hatch. He has slept all night and is fresh. His beard is combed, his silken hair falls smoothly about his shoulders. He looks toward me quickly and his eyes are blank. I don't understand how he can appear so calm. I stare back at him and he turns away.

The storage compartment has been opened and he begins to lift pieces of apparatus out, attaching gravity devices to them and setting them on the floor by the hatchway so that they can be lowered to the ground. When he motions for me to help him I hesitate for a moment; a dense chill passes through me at the sight of the cold, metallic equipment. But after a sharp look from Margus I assist him. Soon the floor of our cabin is covered with instruments.

Margus opens the hatch and sunlight pours into the cabin: a patch of damp, dark green is visible through the opening. He floats down to his waist through the hatchway and stops to give me a silent look; he is searching my face for a challenge. I begin to open my mouth but I know there is nothing for me to do now. I lower my gaze and nod quickly; he drops through to the ground and I follow, landing beside him on the inscribed rock.

The natives are kneeling, their angelic faces touching the dewy ground. Margus bids them rise and they do so. I see that they have brought their chieftains; a small group of older adults, ornately dressed and decorated with greenery, stand by the rock and look up at us in complete adoration. I am humbled at the sight of these men, the leaders of their people, giving themselves to us totally. It is such a gross fraud Margus and I perpetrate, and I want to scream out to them, tell them of our sins and bring them to salvation. I know there is nothing I can do at the moment, though, and I watch as Margus raises his hands over them.

"O holy ones," Margus says to the leaders, and his speaking device has been tuned to make him sound very powerful indeed, "the blessings of the god Arde and I go out to you and, through you, to your people. We have come from the heavens so that we might be with you and that you might honor us. We have come so that the sacred rites might be performed." He straightens up, holding his hands high above his head, fingering a device that causes the sections of apparatus in the ship to float slowly down through the hatchway and settle by the rock. "A great magic will the god Arde and I show you. Go now, but allow ten of your males to remain. We will tell you when to return, and what must be done."

Our theatrical effects work very well, unfortunately, and the natives rise obediently and depart, leaving ten strong young males who come forward, heads lowered. Margus sets them to work arranging the apparatus and clearing out a large area where it is to be assembled. I notice that Margus is watching me closely, and, though it hurts me to do so, I help, quietly praying as I work.

The labor goes slowly. The various sections of the apparatus must be assembled with great care, and there are many delicate adjustments to be made. The native men work like reverential slaves, moving at Margus's every whim.

As the day goes on, it becomes clear to me that Margus has been drinking. His commands become harsher, and a fierce glow has come into his eyes. He is watching me even more closely, and I know that there is a weapon under his robes along with his bottle of alcohol.

Finally, late in the day, all the adjustments have been made, and the apparatus stands finished. It is a mass of twisting tubes and cold receptacles, curving in and around on itself, and I can hardly bear to look at it.

Margus stands upon the flat rock and commands the native males to go into the forest and return with their chieftains and all their people. When they leave he pulls his bottle from beneath his garment and takes a long drink.

"Well, Arde, the first part of the plan is complete. And tomorrow," he says, looking down at me, "we finish the job. But for now, the work is over, and it's time for a bit of recreation." His voice is that of a drunken man. He takes another quick sip and conceals the bottle as the natives come out of the forest.

"Tomorrow," Margus says to them loudly, too loudly, "the sacred rite will be performed. Go into the forest, and collect the sacred fruit of the pampa. Bring much of the sacred fruit. All of you return tomorrow. Go now, but leave for your god the most beautiful daughter of your people, that the god Margus might be with her. Go, and have my blessing."

There is a small amount of confusion, and one of the chieftains, head bowed to his chest, points at me.

Margus, giving me a leering look, laughs and says, "Of course, two daughters of the tribe must be with us, that the god Arde may be with one."

The natives melt quickly into the greenery, leaving two delicate females.

Margus puts his bottle of alcohol under my nose. "Take this," he says, "and drink to the glory of religion. I told you we were gods."

I push the bottle back at him.

His face is flushed. "Which one would you like?"

I close my eyes.

He gives a short laugh. "Come with me, Arde," he says; "you're a damned fool to miss out on this part." He leads me back to the ship, and we float up through the opening. "Go to your sleeping couch," he says, "and pray to your God. Tomorrow we do what we have to with these people, and ignore every one of God's commandments." He laughs, gesturing toward the two female figures waiting below. "And tonight I ignore a special commandment. Twice." His tone of voice sharpens, and he moves the folds of his robe, exposing the weapon hidden there. "Stay here, Arde. I'll be close by. If you try to leave the ship I'll kill you."

He disappears through the opening.

I am certain now that there is no hope of changing Margus's mind about what must be done. I had thought from the beginning of the mission that some way or other I would be able to convert him—my ability in that area was the main reason for the members of the religious minority in the Council choosing me to accompany Margus—but I see now that he is immovable. There is only one alternative for me now. I am saddened by the thought, and I continue to pray for Margus's soul, but the great good of saving the people of this planet justifies my actions. I am filled with a kind of peace at the thought that I will be able to bring these gentle souls to God.

I go to my cubicle and check the hidden compartment where my weapon is hidden. Part of the Council's compromise stated that Margus was to handle the only weapon on this mission, but with the assistance of a religious member of the maintenance crew we were able to see that another was placed on board. It is loaded and set at maximum. I replace it and close the compartment.

I float to my couch and lie back, pressing my fingers to my closed eyes. I empty my mind, and then I begin to pray, speaking the words of the *Karadah*, and I know that God hears me, because my faith sustains me:

*That others be baptised
And thus brought unto Him and live in His love . . .*

Sounds of godless Margus reach my ears from below, and I pray harder, and finally I sleep.

Margus awakens me, roughly, at dawn. His eyes are bloodshot and his face looks worn and tired; but he works with his makeup and is soon ready to descend. Some of the natives have already gathered around the ship.

Margus does not speak to me but I can tell by his manner that he is still serious about carrying out the plan. I decide that I must try one final time to speak with him, to make him see the foolishness and evil of what he is doing.

"Margus," I say, in a conciliatory voice, "please."

His mouth is set.

"Margus, listen to me. This is our last chance. All this time we've spent together, I've prayed for you. I hold no malice toward you, Margus; you know that. Even now, if you would only have faith, we could go down and dismantle the apparatus and—"

His words come out clipped and hard. "Don't try to stop this."

He opens the hatch and drops down to the apparatus.

There is nothing left for me to do. I move quickly to my cubicle and remove my weapon from its casing, tucking it into my garments. I float slowly down to the inscribed rock.

Margus has already begun adjusting the apparatus, and a shudder runs through me at the sight. The natives kneel around us in supplication. They have brought their children, and they wait for the blessing, and for the rite which Margus told them would be performed. I see the two females that Margus was with last night among them; they have a beatific look on their faces which makes me shudder. I want to cry for them.

The religious chieftains, in a line, emerge from the forest bearing a long basket made of woven leaves. The basket is filled with pampa, the sacred fruit of the tribe. The fruit are small spheres, bright orange against the green of the planet. I pull my eyes from the fruit in disgust; Margus glances up at the basket and then turns back to his equipment. The old ones lay the basket down before us and kneel with the others.

Some of the children begin to cry. Margus, I see, is nearly finished.

I adjust the device on my lips to the lowest setting and turn to him. I must speak now. My right hand rests lightly on my weapon, beneath my robe. I whisper into his ear.

"We cannot do this," I begin. "The *Karadah*—"

He twists around, angry. "Arde," he booms, and the natives surrounding us bend their faces to the ground; he adjusts his mouth device to a low setting. "Arde, return to the ship. Lock yourself in your sleeping cubicle." His eyes are ice.

"Margus," I plead, for the final time, "have faith."

He reaches for my arm but my weapon is out. "The pampa—" he says, and he stops.

There is a deep look of disbelief and terror in his eyes as the beam from my weapon cuts into him.

Margus falls to the ground, brushing the apparatus as he falls. I say a prayer for his soul, and am saddened greatly by what I have been forced to do, but now a quiet joy comes over me at the work of salvation I am able to perform. I turn to the natives, humbled and filled with God.

The natives look up at me, puzzled. They stare at the smoking, crumpled body of Margus lying on the grass and they look back up at me. I smile and turn up the speaking device at my lips. I raise my arms over them in blessing. I speak loudly, joyously.

"Rejoice! You are saved!" I cry.

I lower my weapon and begin to fire.

The natives rise and try to flee, their screams filling the morning air. They run to protect their children as I shout at them from my elevation, telling them of the laws and commandments of God, and of the evil plan which Margus was to have carried out—the plan that would have denied them salvation in order that the godless materialists on my planet might gain the valuable elements from within the fruit of the pampa. "The *Karadah* must be followed," I intone, and then I pray over them with the words which have suckled me these past months:

This does the Lord God command His chosen people,
For they are born holy unto Him:
That all men treat themselves as temples of God,
And other men as themselves,
And avoid corruption of flesh and mind
And thus live in His love;
And that this Word be spread by His people,
Who are born in baptism unto Him,
That others be baptised
And thus brought unto Him and live in His love;
And that they be left untouched,
And all that they possess;
And that they be baptised in blood,
And that their blood be the blood of salvation unto them;
For they shall wash in their blood that they be saved.

Some of the natives have reached the edge of the forest but I turn and fire, cutting them down. Sweat drips copiously from my beard. The air is filled with screams and pleading; the blood of salvation covers the earth.

"You are saved!" I cry, thrusting my weapon to the heavens.

The screams fade.

There is silence.

I turn my blaster on Margus's apparatus, the beam cutting easily through it, and then float back up to the spaceship and secure the hatch. I sit in my cushion for a long time with my head thrown back and eyes closed, praying, shaking with an almost sexual joy.

After a while I am calm again and prepare to leave.

There are other villages on this planet; it is time to seek them out. By the time I have saved the people of this world the religious minority at home will be a majority in a great revolution. Other missionaries will be sent, to bring God's Word to other worlds we have exploited in the past.

To all worlds.

There are many planets I will visit; the next is inhabited by small and fierce barbarians.

I lean back in my cushion and contemplate them.

And pray for their salvation.

Hunting the Dragonblood

BY
PATRICK H. ADKINS

"Ready, Grandpa," Emile's excited, youthful voice called from the living room. "I'm all dressed and ready to go."

The old man came suddenly out of his reveries and finished lacing and tying his shoes. He straightened his clothes in front of the mirror, then picked up the old hunting knife in its worn leather sheath from where it lay on the dresser nearby, and carefully adjusted it inside his belt, under his shirt. His self-doubts were leaving him now, and he smiled at his image; he was starting to look more like Big Jason Townshed now.

His smile broadened. Not quite, he thought; he'd have been the laughingstock of the boys in the old days. He didn't even have a decently ragged suit of clothes anymore.

"I'm waiting, Grandpa," the boy called.

"Coming, boy, I'm coming." The man's voice had a new note of assurance in it.

He was readjusting the knife as the boy met him in the living room. "What's that, Grandpa? Under your shirt?"

The man unsnapped a strap on the scabbard and pulled the knife free.

"A knife! A real knife," the boy cried, almost dancing around the old man in his excitement. "Like they used to have. Can I see it? Please?"

The man proffered the scarred relic, finding himself saying, "Careful with it, son," even though the blade was dull beyond sharpening and the point rounded from long years of use.

"What's it for? In case somebody tries to take our dragonblood from us?"

Grandpa laughed. "Not likely these days, Em"—he always avoided using the boy's proper name; what could Crissy have been thinking of to call a boy Emile?—"but when I was your age, my father always carried a gun when he went on a hunt. A big black automatic pistol; he had a government license for it, too. A lot of blooders did, then."

"Did he shoot anybody?"

Grandpa shook his head. "But he needed it all the same. If he hadn't had it, you can bet somebody would have tried to steal his finds. It was rough back then, boy, not like today. My father had some close scrapes in those days. . . ."

"*Your* father?" the boy said slowly, as though only now realizing what the man had said. "*Your* father hunted dragonblood?"

Grandpa had taken back his knife and tucked it away inside his clothes again. "My father and his father before him," he said as he began gathering and bagging the sandwiches he had made earlier that morning. "That makes you the fifth of the line to hunt Ole Johnny's bounty, my boy; I guess we can count your mother. She spent a lot of time hunting with me, back when she was a girl."

Emile had followed him into the kitchen, and Grandpa handed him a large canteen to carry.

Back in the living room, Grandpa pulled his cane from its holder near the door. "The sun's been up for almost two hours. Fifty years ago, the roads would be aswarm with hunters by now. Let's go, Em."

The old man carefully locked the door behind them as they left the house. The street was indeed bustling, not with blooders but with men and women leaving for work, children procrastinating their way to school. A departing neighbor tooted the horn of her steamcar and waved at them as she backed out of her driveway.

"But what's the knife for, Grandpa?" Emile wanted to know.

"For digging. Fingers wear out pretty quick, and a shovel gets awful heavy. But let's not talk till we're away from the neighbors. That's the first rule of the dragonblooder—a shut mouth."

Emile nodded as though worldly-wise, but even as he said it the man felt suddenly foolish. The only reason left for secrecy was to avoid the scorning mirth of the people he had to live near. But why shouldn't they laugh at him? Cowboys and sailors remain heroic as long as they stay put in their own times; only a child or a fool would try to be a cowboy or a dragonblooder in 2183.

As they walked along the narrow pedestrian path, a group of children swarmed out of one of the nearby adobe trackhouses. Almost immediately one of the children spotted them. "Dragonman! Dragonman! Where are you going?" the first shouted, and the others took it up as a chant.

Emile started toward them, his fists clenched, but Grandpa held him back. "Just keep walking, son. Fools. There're fools everywhere."

And of all ages, he thought. Like him. Why was he doing this, building up the boy's hopes so? The hunting times were gone, and he was still hunting, even though it had been years since he had made a find. Why didn't he admit that it wasn't his eyes? It was all gone now; all the dragonblood had been found long ago, and there just wasn't any more left. . . .

He looked down at the boy beside him. He'd be ten years old in a month or so. Why hadn't he kept his old fool's mouth shut, instead of building up hopes that could never be fulfilled? Especially now, with Em's father only a few months dead and his mother away—with that man.

He shook his head slowly, not even aware that his thoughts had been translated into physical movement. He had understood Crissy better when she was a child, when she was Em's age. Once the glands started working, he thought, there was no hope for a man to under-stand a woman.

But thinking this way wouldn't do any good. He needed the money that even the smallest find would bring, especially now that Em was living with him. He pulled himself erect. The boy wouldn't be disap-pointed, he told himself. Ole Johnny had sown his seeds too widely and too well. No one would ever find it all, and with his know-how and Em's bright young eyes, they'd get their share—besides, he thought suddenly, there's almost no competition left.

Em had been watching a dirigible drifting languidly across the hori-zon. "How far do we have to go?" he asked after a few minutes. They had walked four blocks and were crossing a street.

"A little farther. We want to get away from our own neighborhood. Besides, I've been this way lots of times; even as bad as my eyes are, I'd have seen traces if they were here."

"Can we talk yet?"

Grandpa nodded. "If you keep your voice down."

Emile took a sudden deep breath, as though stifling the loud words that had been ready to spill out, then proceeded to speak slowly. "Just talk, Grandpa. Tell me everything about dragonblood."

The old man smiled, reaching out and mussing the boy's blond hair. "You've already asked a thousand questions, and I've already tried to answer them."

"But tell me more. Tell me about the old days, when you hunted every day."

Grandpa sighed, resolved to the task of dredging up still more memo-ries. "You've got to remember, Em, that when I came along blooding had been around a long time already. It was already scarce, and worth almost as much as it is today. Why, when I was a boy, my father use to go into stores and pay for things with his finds. . . ."

"How much is it worth?" the boy wanted to know. "More than gold?"

The man nodded. "A little more than gold, if you go by volume—by size. A whole lot more by weight, though; about thirty-five dollars a gram, last time I checked. That's one of the reasons it's so valuable, its lightness. If you know how to handle it, you can make it almost as strong as steel . . . well, maybe not that strong, but as strong as a good, hard wood. But it still weighs only a fraction of what wood would weigh, and you can melt it over a fire and mold it to any shape you want."

He ran his fingers through his hair as he spoke. "Why, it's the most versatile stuff in the solar system, and practically indestructible. If it's been made right, it'll last more than a thousand years buried in the ground, not losing its shape at all. Steel would rust. Wood would rot. But not dragonblood. It just stays there, waiting to be found and used over again.

"Think of it, son, the blood of the dragons—the dinosaurs. Our ancestors dug it out of the heart of the earth, where it had been buried for millions and millions of years. They had so much of it they never even thought about the way they used it—they made everything out of it, and most of the time they just threw it away afterwards, or burned it as rubbish. Even their word for it—they called it *plastic*—meant cheap, worthless. Of course a few knew better, like Ole Johnny. We owe him a whole lot, son."

"What color is it? I've never seen any, you know."

"Any color and every color. If you know what you're doing, you can make it any color at all—green, or yellow like the sun, or black as night. That's another reason it's worth so much. Then, of course, there are some medicines that can only be produced from dragonblood. That's where all of it goes these days, but in my father's time rich people bought it. It makes beautiful jewelry, rings, necklaces, whatever you like, in any color or shape, and so light you don't even know you're wearing it. That was before the government made it illegal for private people to own."

"Did you ever have any dragonblood jewelry?"

"I had a ring, a big blue-black one carved like a lion. The most beautiful ring you've ever seen, Em. You've seen pictures of lions, haven't you? A big, roaring lion's head. My father had it especially made for me, when I turned eighteen."

"What happened to it?" The boy's eyes mixed excitement with anxiety.

The man shrugged. "The government got it, like most of the others. Just about everybody turned it in, I guess. It wouldn't be right to use something that precious for jewelry when it could save lives. Still," he mused, "I wish I hadn't had to give it up. I wish you could have seen it."

"Are we ready to start hunting now?" Emile was looking around at the adobe sameness on each side of the street.

"A little farther."

"Why are you smiling, Grandpa?"

"Just remembering. I went with my father one time when he was shopping for a new visiscreen. He'd forgotten his cashcard, and the salesman had already punched up the sale. Well, my father just pulled a huge hunk of blood out of his pocket. The salesman's eyes got as big as saucers as my father took out his pocket knife—they were still legal then, you know—and began carving off a piece. 'If you have a scale . . .' he started to say, and the salesman said, 'Yes, *sir!*' "

They laughed together. "But what happened to all the money, Grandpa?"

The man shrugged. "It goes fast, when you've got more than you know what to do with and don't expect your source to run out." He paused for a moment, lost in thought, then said, "But we lived good then, Em." He was smiling. "We lived *damn* good."

They walked in silence for a few minutes.

"But what are we looking for?" Em asked.

"Traces. Traces of old roads that are covered over now, or old streams or ponds. At least that's what we looked for before these damn houses started covering the traces up. A long time ago, in Ole Johnny's time, most of the country was still open. It's only in the last hundred years or so that the government houses have spread over the land. Before that most of the country was still woods and farms, with just roads passing through. That's how Johnny got around so much, I guess."

"I don't understand. What do traces look like?"

"You look for differences in the land. Most of the old roads have been kept up, or built over. They're no good. They've been hunted for centuries, or at least since hunting started. But some of the old roads were allowed to go to waste and eventually the wind covered them over. You have to look for a straight, narrow strip of land, higher than the rest. That's one sign. Some of the old ponds will look like depressions in the surrounding ground. One trick is to look for old trees— really old, a hundred years or more. They were here before the houses started to push them out, so you'll know Johnny could have been in the area. He usually stayed pretty close to the old roads, or in places that were parks then. The old trees will be bigger than all the others— not just tall, but big all around, and they'll have limbs that have been snapped off by lightning."

The boy nodded to show that he understood at least some of what his grandfather was saying.

"Keep your eyes open. Mine aren't much good now, even with these glasses, but I'll try to show you just what to look for."

As they walked, the man began pointing out nearby trees and announcing their probable ages.

"Most of the streets in this area aren't very old—maybe thirty or forty years. All except Meyers Avenue, about two blocks that way. It's old, so this may be a good place to begin looking, since Johnny wouldn't have had to get too far from the highway. People could have come here hundreds of years ago, and that means there could be dragonblood buried somewhere around here."

"Is that an old tree, Grandpa?" Emile asked, pointing to the rear of one of the adobe houses.

"Could be," the man answered slowly, peering through the thick lenses of his glasses. "Let's get a closer look." They walked along the side of the building. "It looks old, all right. You've got good eyes, Em." They moved closer, until they were standing beneath the branches of the huge oak. Grandpa pointed up. "See that branch. See how thick it is, thick as most trees ever get. See the one near it, broken off. It's old, all right, maybe a hundred and fifty."

"Where do we dig? Around the tree?"

"Never can tell where Johnny planted the stuff—" Grandpa was saying when a voice from behind them interrupted.

"What do you two want?" demanded a woman standing at the rear of the house.

The man stepped a little in front of the boy, a reflexive action, as though to protect him. "Sorry to bother you, ma'am," he began, already feeling foolish in front of the woman's unwavering gaze. "My grandson and I were out walking when we saw this tree. You see, I used to be a dragonblooder years ago. . . ." He started to fumble his words. "I thought the boy might like to see how it was done. If you wouldn't mind our poking around a bit, we'd be happy to share anything we might find with you. You know, there could be some blood buried here. . . ."

The woman was shaking her head. "No you don't. I won't have my yard torn up. Go someplace else."

She stood on the steps, watching them as they made their way back toward the street.

"Not like it used to be," the man told Emile when they reached the front walk again. He shrugged, then smiled. "Oh, well, we've still got a lot of walking in us."

He tried not to admit that the woman was right. After a few minutes he started to whistle, one of the old tunes, one his father had whistled. In between the whistling he continued to talk, old stories mixed with blooding lore. Remembering is an old man's occupation, he thought. He kept talking so he wouldn't have to admit to himself that those times were no more.

Twice the boy pointed out trees, and they paused to inspect them, only to find that they were not quite old enough to warrant further investigation. They stopped at one of the small open spaces that served as a neighborhood playground.

"Couldn't we try digging here? There might be some dragonblood buried here, couldn't there be, Grandpa?"

"Not likely, Em." The man shook his head slowly. "Everything's so different now, the traces aren't even left."

"Couldn't we dig anyway, just in case?"

The man glanced at his watch. More time had passed than he had realized. It was after eleven o'clock already. "Okay, Em. We'll give it a try. Let's start back near the fence and work toward the street."

Grandpa twisted the handle of his cane and pulled out the long, thin probing rod built swordlike into the cane, a remnant of his last prosperous years. "Push down on it like this," he explained, "so that it goes in fifteen or twenty centimeters—you don't have to go deep here, then do it again farther over. Keep to a pattern, so you cover the whole yard."

He let the boy take over. Emile was smart, eager, the old man thought; in time he could become a skillful blooder, one of the best—if there was anything left to be found. A few minutes later the boy struck something solid.

"Okay, when you hit something, tap it lightly—like this." He took hold of the rod and demonstrated. "By tapping it you can tell if you've hit blood or something else—metal, glass, wood, rock. You don't have to dig it up. Hear it? *Tink, tink.* That's glass, but it sounds flat, not hollow, so it's not a bottle, or a broken one. They made bottles with dragonblood caps and stoppers, so you've got to feel around it, this way." He skillfully probed from different directions and angles. "No, no blood down there . . ." He looked at the boy. "Want to dig it up and see for yourself?"

Emile nodded and Grandpa turned his back to the street, so that no one passing by would see his old knife. He could explain it to the police, of course; he'd done it often enough in the past, and it certainly wasn't much of a weapon anymore. Still, he preferred to avoid distasteful situations.

The boy fell to digging vigorously, and after a few moments unearthed a shard from a broken bottle. The man patted his shoulder. Returning the knife to his grandfather, the boy took up the probing rod again, slowly working his way back and forth across the grass until most of the yard had been explored.

"Best give it up, Em," the man said. "You're not going to find anything that near the street. This just isn't a good place to look. When dragonblood first became really scarce and valuable, people went wild. They dug up their back yards, their front yards, any place they could get at. The chances against just digging anywhere and making a find are too great; you've got to cut down the odds some.

"My father made a study of it. He collected old maps and reference books, researched everything before he started on a hunt. He knew just where to look to find a dump, or the old roads, parks, factories—any place likely to have a store. Even that wouldn't work today, I'm afraid. You've got to be lucky, too."

"We'll find some yet, Grandpa," Emile said.

He let the boy rest for a while, then they started walking again, past one adobe trackhouse after another. The stretches of silence became longer. Finally Emile spotted another old tree, this time near the street, where no outraged homeowner would be likely to accost them. Grandpa showed the boy how to sound out the trunk for hollow places by tapping against it with the hilt of the knife.

"Sometimes an old tree will heal over an open place," he explained, "and Ole Johnny might have left something inside for whoever can find it. Look for old scars."

There were no hollow spots. The boy climbed up into the tree to search the larger limbs and inspect the nooks and crannies, ignoring Grandpa's half-hearted protests.

"There could be dragonblood up here," the boy said hopefully.

"Ole Johnny made his deposits everywhere and anywhere."

Emile found nothing in the tree, but he insisted on probing the ground around its base, then upon digging down to the object Grandpa had already identified as a buried root from the tree.

When he had finished, the two sat under the tree and ate lunch. The boy was visibly disappointed.

"I'm sorry, Em," the man said. "We shouldn't be doing this. The chances of our finding anything are almost nil."

The boy shook his head. "No, Grandpa. It's just hard work today, that's all. We'll find some if we keep looking."

For the most part they ate in silence. Finally Emile said, "Grandpa, was there really an Ole Johnny?"

The man looked up. "Johnny Litterbug?" He shrugged his shoulders wearily. "All the old blooders believed in him, Em. And it makes sense, when you stop to think about it. Why else would so much dragonblood be hidden away in the damnedest places? They say he used to travel all over the country, hiding it wherever he could, because he knew we'd run out some day and all that would be left would be what he'd left for us. Nobody understood him then. They say they even passed laws against him, trying to make him stop. But that didn't stop him. He just kept stashing dragonblood all over the country, so that we could find it today, when we really need it."

They started walking again, looking for traces, finding none. Time and again the boy pointed out trees that were too young, begged to be allowed to probe some small stretch of ground.

I'm a fool, the man thought; an old fool who can't adjust to the present. I have no right to do this to Em, build up his hopes like this. We can make it the way everybody else does, make the budget stretch a little more, live on the government allowance. It's a different world, all changed, and I've got to change too.

But they kept walking, kept looking. The afternoon passed slowly in weary legs and growing disappointment, until at last it was almost time to start home.

"What's that?" the boy asked, pointing across the street. "They've torn down a building, haven't they? Let's go look, Grandpa. Maybe nobody has dug under it."

"It's not old enough, Em. They didn't build adobes then." He followed the boy across the street. "Okay, Em, but we go home after this one."

Most of the adobe bricks had been carted away or reduced to fine rubble, and men had already been at work on the foundation with sledge hammers. The workers had probably already left for the day.

Grandpa stopped suddenly just in front of the broken concrete, staring silently at it. "You may be right, son," he said slowly. "Look closely at the foundation. The concrete's different from what we use today—a different mix, I guess. That's not the way it's done anymore. This foundation is old. They must have built the adobe on the foundation of a much older building."

They walked in among the broken pieces of concrete. "It's probably not old enough, even so," the old man found himself saying. "Don't get your hopes up, Em. But it is worth a try."

He twisted the handle on his cane, brought out the probing rod. "We'll start on one side, work across. They use to have plumbing pipes made from dragonblood. Of course, they could have been taken out years ago, if they were ever here, and the original building might not have been old enough—I can't tell exactly, but let's try."

He tried not to let the boy see how excited he was. Emile took the rod, but Grandpa stood right beside him, directing every move. Slowly they made their way across the property, sinking the rod deeper than before. "Pipes would be half a meter or a little more down," the man explained. They moved the probe over a few centimeters, sank it into the ground again. The man kicked or pried large pieces of concrete out of the way. Each time the rod sank, the man literally held his breath.

The rod struck something. Grandpa shoved Emile aside, took hold of the probe. He raised and lowered it again, tapping softly two, three times.

Emile's voice was hushed. "What is it?"

The old man shook his head slowly, his shoulders suddenly drooping now that the suspense was gone. "Aluminum. An aluminum pipe. That means it's not old enough."

Emile was crestfallen. "Couldn't there be other pipes, of dragon-blood?"

"No, not likely."

"I'm going to keep trying," the boy said, taking the probing rod back. His grandfather didn't have the heart to stop him. He stood aside, weak now, feeling all of his years. The boy continued slowly across the yard. Again the rod struck something hard, and a third time. All three were aluminum. At each metallic clink the boy looked up expectantly, only to see his grandfather slowly shake his head.

"Let's go home, Em," the man said softly. "I guess Ole Johnny's bounty has finally run out."

Emile kept working. When he had finished crossing the lot, he began to slowly circle the foundation. Grandpa sat down on a piece of concrete, watching, thinking. He'd find the extra money some way, or somehow make the money stretch even further. He put his head in his hands.

The old man looked up suddenly, a puzzled expression on his face. He rose slowly, frowning as he walked toward the boy. "What did you just hit?" he asked.

"Another pipe. Like the others."

"Do it again. Let me listen."

The boy retraced his path, located the place again, near the edge of the foundation. Grandpa listened carefully as the probe tapped against the object. Then he nodded. "Yes, it's a pipe, but it's odd. It's not aluminum; it's cast iron. That's what they used before aluminum—before dragonblood pipes, too."

The boy continued probing around the pipe. "It's a big one, Grandpa," he said. "And it ends here, I think."

"But it doesn't make sense. . . ." The man's puzzled eyes studied the contours of the ground. "It could have been above the ground at one time, Em—see the way the earth slopes suddenly away, as though this area has been built up. . . ."

The boy had already taken the knife from him and was on his knees digging. He had to use his hands to pull the dirt out of the hole. He dug down twenty centimeters before hitting the pipe. "I was right," he said. "It does end here, Grandpa. There might be some dragonblood in it, couldn't there be? You said Ole Johnny liked to put it in strange places."

"What's that under it, Em?" The old man stepped closer. "It looks like concrete—a cement slab? Maybe it's some kind of drainage pipe. . . . There must have been some other building here, before the foundation. . . ."

The boy worked quickly, until he could get the blade of the knife into the open end of the large pipe. He scooped out black mud, and then a shapeless glob, black with mud, spotted with color. "What's this?" the boy asked.

Grandpa reached out, touched it, unbelieving. "Em," he said slowly, "it's dragonblood—dragonblood paper!" His voice faltered. "They used to make a special paper out of it, to wrap things in—food, candy, other things. I've never seen it before. So well preserved . . . my father used to talk about it. They used a low grade of blood. I've never seen any before. . . ." He peeled off a long, thin sheet that had once been, perhaps, a potato chip package.

"It's good, though, isn't it?" the boy asked, pulling out more, now reaching in up to his elbow. "There's more, Grandpa—much more!"

"Yes, it's good—any dragonblood is worth money today. I just can't believe it. You found the dragonblood, Em. . . ."

The boy's dirt-streaked face looked up, grinning. "You just stopped believing, Grandpa; that's all. But it was really you. You knew the pipe was different, or I wouldn't have dug."

"The pipe must have preserved it," the old man was saying. Then he dropped to his knees beside the boy. "There's so much of it—must be hundreds and hundreds of pieces. Somebody went to a lot of trouble to store it like this," he said, a tinge of awe in his voice.

The boy looked up again. "Johnny must have done it—Ole Johnny, huh, Grandpa?"

Big Jason Townshed threw his arm around his grandson's shoulders and hugged the boy to him.

The Sound of Hawkwings Dissolving

BY
STEVE RASNIC TEM

When my hawk discovered her, Ellen was slumped semiconscious on the other side of the yellowed windowpane. Her arm crawled up the glass, stiff-fingered, matching my hawk's motions stroke for stroke, claw for claw. She'd always been like that on a high: playful, morbid.

I had arrived outside Ellen's third-story window only a few minutes after my hawk. I hung upside down from the awning over the window, staring past the hawk and into Ellen's face. She hadn't seen me yet; she couldn't until my familiar flew in, and I followed it. Her looks gave me second thoughts about entering at all: sallow skin, lined and ancient-looking, paper-thin flesh angling into bone. Stringy black hair. I'd almost forgotten this side of her.

She jerked the window open as I knew she would, but whether out of some sort of childish curiosity or suicidal impulse I couldn't be sure. Turning abruptly from the rush of the hawk, she began pacing the room restlessly, then sat on one section of the semicircular green sofa, rearranged items on the zebra-striped coffee table, got up, stared listlessly at Chagall's "I and the Village" on a side wall, paced, rubbed her hands together.

As I drifted through the window her gray cat began an agitated pacing by the back wall. She cursed it vehemently. I moved a phantom hand along Ellen's throat, sensed watering eyes, runny nose, a cold burn buzzing across her body. No question—she was junk sick.

She stared out into the space where my face would be. Her eyes seemed to have nothing to do with the rest of her features, independent, moving with their own life. Her face had been taken over by the heroin. When my face and body began to congeal into visibility for her she screamed. My hawk landed on the back of the sofa and, its wings gently fluttering, watched her cat. The room seemed to pulse. Sometimes I resent the extreme sensitivity my ghost body can have.

Oh, I'll use the word, although "ghost" is hopelessly inadequate as a label. I use it ironically, even mockingly, but words do have their limitations. What else might I call myself?

She blinked, licked her cracked lips. Her entire head quivered. She held her arms tightly in the sudden cold I knew she must be feeling, but which I would never feel again. I would have allowed her to hear strange music, rattling chains, and moans, but I was trying to be kind. I knew I would try for only a short time.

With a yellow dress hanging loosely from her shoulders, a white-bag purse around her thin wrist, she walked with me into the street. An old man with dark matted hair lay on the sidewalk, clutching a stained paper bag. She didn't notice. I grabbed her face with my hand and looked into her empty eyes, seeking the beautiful green I remembered, but the irises were dull. Her eyes used to make me able to imagine myself at her birthplace, a southern farm, cutting hay, gathering walnuts.

She had adjusted to my presence. There are few surprises for the heroin addict. Perhaps she thought I was a hallucination. But at least I was a familiar hallucination, I suppose, something she could talk to.

"*I want something from you, you know. That's what I'm here for,*" I told her, but I wasn't sure it registered at that point. We were in an all-night cafe, and I'm sure the half-dozen other patrons could hear her speaking, seemingly to herself, but she wasn't the only one talking to herself in the cafe that night. People ignored her.

Then her eyes seemed to clear; she looked at me directly. "Well . . . I don't have anything left to give."

As yet I didn't trust her enough to tell her about the child. I merely watched her in silence, trying to feel her out. She was actually worse than I remembered, talking aimlessly to me; I wasn't even sure she knew who I was. She talked on and on without focus, a listless monologue.

My hawk was hidden in the shadows above the dark blue cafe curtains, a still gray shadow.

"My father was kind to us girls, but he certainly made us work. He certainly did. I loved him so. We'd spend all day gathering walnuts and he'd walk us home, an arm for each of us. He called us his princesses, bought us lovely blouses and hard red candy." She smiled until the muscles tightened in her face, and leaned forward conspiratorially, "Many men loved me, so many, but he was nicer than any man I ever met. He looked good even at fifty, wore the same size clothes he did in high school."

I felt a twinge of jealousy and was surprised. She still had a piece of me. I tried to make my question less personal, anonymous: *"Do you remember any of your lovers?"*

"No . . . no, none of them. Lovers come and go. You only really remember your family. I remember my sister Anne. Eloise . . . my mother. And my father."

We left the cafe and headed down Monument Avenue, my hawk fluttering above our heads.

Monument is lined with buildings of various styles: Spanish alongside Gothic alongside English Country Manor. Years ago it was the rich suburb; students and the welfare old now rent sub-divided rooms and apartments. I remembered standing in an alley after walking blocks—Ellen and I had fought. I listened to a violinist play sections from Vivaldi in a back window above. Then his wife screamed at him. I had been drinking again—it seemed as if she were shrieking the building down. The violinist screamed back; there seemed to be a violent scuffling. The violin came sailing out of the window and I ran.

"Ellen, don't you remember me?"

She turned and looked up into my dark hair line, the widow's peak. She smiled and threw back her hair, laughing. "Mark, where have you been?"

We walked out beyond the museum, to the park, where paddleboats rocked in anchor at a pier. I felt unexpectedly affectionate at that moment, and held her tightly. I wasn't sure what she would feel of my ghost form—I'd never done this before. I wondered cynically if she could even tell the difference between me and a living body. Everyone's a specter when you're up on junk. But although it was cold she wasn't noticing it, and her junk shivers seemed to have stopped. My hawk looped around us; I needed its proximity to hold her this way. Once again I was amazed by the hawk's intuitiveness. I hadn't even had to signal it.

Although ghosts don't really breathe, we do have a sensation as of inhalation/exhalation. Memories of our past lives make themselves known this way. That is . . . the closest thing I can think of is colors. Our memories manifest themselves as colors.

I breathed in this manner the yellow of my past life with her, the silver of the days after I left her, back into imaginary lungs, and let the months since my death drift out from my phantom tongue, drape the maples, enter ghostly reflections far out on the lake. Ghosts travel widely—I breathed out the chinook I rode that first time I was in phantom, then burning in Mexican desert, then cold under city asphalt, imagined heat, imagined cold, then with lovers in a park far away but similar to this one. Breathing them in and out, inhalation and exhalation, the colors lingering in the park about treetops and hedgerows before finally fading. A passerby would have considered them mirages, an effect brought on by some chance arrangement of streetlights and fog.

Birds fluttered in the maple tops, no doubt disturbed by the presence of my hawk.

A young man loitered on a park bench in front of us. In the streetlight: a hairless face, plucked eyebrows, almond skin. Ellen walked over and sat beside him. I felt very much the voyeur. They exchanged words, money, an envelope.

She was quiet as we returned to her apartment. I wanted to hold her, cover her face with spectral kisses, but my hawk held back. I knew he wouldn't consent to those special maneuvers a familiar must perform before I could make love to Ellen. His intent was obvious from the way he held back, just out of the range of the streetlights. I felt myself dimming; was he going to make me disappear? I followed Ellen back to her apartment, a few steps behind, like a pale shadow. She spoke with her head up, out into the darkness—a monologue again, although I knew it was vaguely addressed to me. I answered her, in the same way, a distant echo.

"You were always right, Ellen. I couldn't last. Two months after I left here."

"I'd have loved several if I could. I'd have loved you, Mark. But deep down, I knew you weren't what I wanted."

"She wasn't anything special, no more than you. But it was the accumulation of hurts and humiliations, you know? You never quite loved me. I don't think you could ever decide."

"Father always made us girls feel good, protected, you know? He was always thinking up new things for us to do; we were never at a loss for entertainment. All my lovers have been so boring, in a way. I couldn't find anyone I really wanted, who was really entertaining to me. But they couldn't understand that."

"I'd grown up thinking no one could love me, so maybe I was hard for you or anyone to convince. It happened again—another woman walked out on me. That's all I could think about."

"I tried to get interested, I really did, but things would all go wrong, so I'd stop being interested, and then I'd be bored. There was never anything to do or say. When I'd say something everything would go all wrong and I'd just have to shut up. I'd just have to sit in my room, there was never anything to do or say."

"*She couldn't talk. Seems she felt guilty she didn't love me. I pressed her, and she left. The waiter came and I didn't know what to say.*"

"I was kind to them all but they still couldn't understand."

"*I started off slow with the sleeping pills . . .*"

"They would get mad and say I didn't feel anything for them."

"*. . . just wanting to scare myself this time I think . . .*"

"But I was always kind."

"*. . . but, Ellen, I went too far.*"

"I let them take me to bed; what else did they want?"

"*I couldn't come back. . . .*"

"I was always kind."

"*I couldn't wake up, Ellen.*"

"I stayed quiet for them."

"*Ellen, it was too easy to sleep.*"

In the alley three men in dark coats were rolling a drunk, "working the hole," as I remembered the slang. The lush came up slowly, and the biggest man kicked him in the mouth. Ellen passed the coughing and spitting at a fast trot.

I lay with her that night on her balcony; she never could sleep indoors during the summer. Red glow over the rooftops. Sweet flowers in the air. My hawk stayed distant, perched on the back of the sofa. Ellen breathed into me with jackal's breath.

She ate an early breakfast in a cafe on Grace Street. Or rather, she ordered it. We had been talking about large meals we remembered with our families, which made her think of late breakfasts with young boys she was dating, who presented these meals as if they had invented this romantic new idea. She was getting jittery. Looking over her shoulder, picking up and replacing the fork and spoon, rearranging her napkin. She left early, and I followed her at a distance. I really believe she had forgotten I was there.

I was feeling playful, hiding in alleys and dark entrance foyers, knowing all the time that no one could see me anyway. I draped myself over a tavern sign, hung strings of myself down, breathing memory in and out so that I must have resembled a multicolored negligee. A drunk stumbled into me and thought he was choking to death, swinging his arms, fighting imagined cobwebs, and my hawk circling him. The moon seemed pierced by a steepletop. I imagined a score of pale bodies spilling from its ruptured center, end over end. Landing in the street, they became pigeons.

A man accosted Ellen in front of her building: "Are you anywhere?" Obviously a friend, I thought.

She shook her head, "I'm good for a couple of days." He lurched past me and my hawk sideswiped his head. He ducked, clutched the back of his head, looked around confused.

My hawk reentered her apartment through the window, but I chose to float in through a rent in the wallpaper, between two virgins and a goat.

I watched her shoot up.

I drifted over and leaned against the nape of her neck, clutching her, shoulder muscles with imagined claws. The hawk alighted on her shoulder and dug his claws in. I wrapped myself around her, bleeding her pain and relief up into me, my arms, the dust blowing behind my phantom eyes, the great emptiness swelling inside me. I really wanted to know what she was feeling, this once. I brought up the memories of my human limbs and body, turning my form a hazy blue. I sensed the morphine claw, digging into the backs of my remembered legs, climbing up and flowering in the neck, muscle and tissues floating up from bone. And a remembered self-condemnation coming up in a red wave: "*Always the victim, Mark?*"

Ellen seemed to be feeling very little. After so many times it's like eating breakfast.

She moaned, easing back against the wall. Her eyelids closed in slow motion. Soon she was asleep. I asked my hawk to perch near her, to protect her, while I dissolved myself into pure strands of silver ectoplasm. Even ghosts need to recharge at times.

But the colors of memory would allow me no rest. Silver: nights with Vivaldi on the player, when Ellen would leap from her chair and drag me, dancing across the old violet rug, her hair swinging side to side, eyes flirtatious. This would pass in minutes; she'd fall back lazily into her chair. The dancing had been planned, a deliberate attempt to stir herself up. Orange: her days waiting for the next fix, three times a day like meals, everything else an excuse, a pretense, until she got her fix. White: nights reduced down to Vivaldi, and Dylan, and watching over her body slumped on the couch, lying on the rug. My arms too tired to hold her. Green: days shrunk down to Dylan, and Vivaldi, and so much booze my throat was coming up bile; fantasies of the welfare apartments across the street exploding, the tenants hanging inside, naked and eyes vacant. Gray: a few bouts with uremic poisoning, feeling swollen, the room smelling like a toilet. Brown: days she spent searching out a meet, working her outfit, dropper and needle, wrapping a collar; her nights sleeping, an occasional job.

I hoped to be gone before I discovered how she was supporting herself these days. She couldn't be hitting up her dad anymore, and I was out of the picture. I remembered her a year before, talking about white slavery as if it were a game.

"Ellen, you've got my baby in you. That's why I came back."

She looked awful—her face dark and insectlike, eyes too far gone for tears. "I don't want a baby now, Mark. Maybe later. Why don't we wait awhile, let me get over this little habit of mine."

"Ellen . . . Ellen, listen to me. It's too late; you've got the baby now, and it's well along. Listen to me."

"I'll kick it soon; I know I will. We can get married, Mark. Buy us a little farm. The baby can grow up right."

I sensed my hawk ruffle his back feathers, turning his head anxiously back and forth. *"Ellen, no. It's too late. You've got to do something now. You're carrying my son, and he's . . ."*

"We'll have a big wedding. My father might come to give me away. . . ."

The hawk beat a frantic tattoo with its wings.

"Ellen, my son's an addict!"

We took a bus into the country, just like old times. I thought maybe it would make a difference. She'd be relaxed; I could get to her then. I'd talk her into seeing a doctor.

We kept the hawk hidden in her picnic basket. She thought it a fine game, and giggled constantly, poking it lightly with her fingers through the dropcloth. My hawk remained still.

"Mark, I'm cold." People were watching her suspiciously.

I put an intangible arm around her, wondering what manner of comfort it might provide. The bus eased out to the interstate.

An old man sat in front of us, his smile taking up the slack in his cheeks. He nodded when we first sat down, tilted his head in a mechanical way. A brief reach to his shoulder told me he was going to die in a few months, much pain erupting through the joints and chest muscles. The bus let us off at a side road, then we walked about a mile.

Ellen's body was like a white frond submerged in the creek. Fluffed out, and buoyant, but with occasional dark streaks. I sat on the bank, the hawk at my feet studying the opposite bank for signs of small game. Abruptly it took off and began circling the water.

Ellen looked good in the water. I wanted to hold her, but I suspected that if I got closer my desire would vanish. Better to watch her. I had loved her, perhaps I still did. But she had always demanded I be someone else, that I be strict with her, then that I give her warmth even as she clawed my face, that I keep her in line, that I hold her when she was sick. I always became the wrong thing with her; it was always something else I needed to be. My love began to drain away; but not completely, never completely. There was always a strand that held me.

When I'd killed myself I was angry with her, lying there, pain like tiny bombs exploding behind my eyeballs, down the optic nerve and into my gut. I kept seeing her face.

"I got tired of waiting, Ellen. You were never going to get yourself clean."

I drifted over to an outcropping of rock and sat there. I could see the top of Ellen's head, the occasional stroke of a pale arm. She wouldn't be able to see me; my hawk was too far away.

I remembered an old man I had watched die a few months before, in Colorado. He had bent over, hacked, coughed blood. No one else around, but me, the specter, the phantom, the ghostly observer. A three year old girl was beaten in Chicago by her drunken father; I hung against the door and watched. A West Virginia miner died in a cave-in beside me.

They had all died on the same note, the same vibration, something only a ghost might sense. I could remember my hawk trilling with that same terror as the deaths occurred, that fear of ending.

My son.

I had always wished for him, but was too embarrassed to admit it. The women I knew had always made fun of the idea. Ellen said it was male pride. Having a child. Strange as it seemed at the time, I would have liked to have given birth myself. But now . . . ghosts aren't easily embarrassed.

A whiteness of protoplasm, squirming under the sun and sucking air.

My son wrapped his arms around my phantom legs, buried a dark head against me, beckoning my hawk with his free hand. I manufactured new memories, and made colorful shimmers around him. I remembered picking him up and burying my face in his soft belly, kissing him wetly until he giggled. His face was large, seeming to cover the sun. Soft green eyes and a widow's peak. I put him on my shoulder and carried him up the hill to watch the sunset. We sat in the dirt and played marbles: catseyes, steelies, rolling off under the grass, frantically searching for them. We played hide and seek behind the white house and hid in terror from my father. But we held each other and there was no pain. We built a fortress out of sticks at the creek mouth. He broke the skin on his knee and I held him, applied iodine, told jokes and tickled him so he wouldn't cry anymore. I gave him a bath in the kitchen sink; he giggled and kicked violently, throwing soapy water into my face, burning my eyes. But I laughed too. He fell asleep on my bare chest wearing just his diaper. I fell asleep too and Ellen had to put us both to bed. These new memories I had made spun lazily around us, their colors gradually fading until they had disappeared.

We rode the bus into Richmond with the spirit of my son between us, although Ellen couldn't see him. He fell asleep against me.

Back in her apartment Ellen sucked air, hard, and main-lined one into her leg before I could stop her. My son awoke, startled and crying, and began to fade.

Minutes later I could sense his pain inside Ellen's womb. My hawk was soaring through the apartment, circling, screeching.

I extended an appendage and touched Ellen's face: her eyes wide, cheeks swelling, fingers enlarged. I could feel an unpleasant burning.

I sensed that odd vibration in my hawk's wings, the trilling, the high-pitched shriek as it crashed into the living room wall, crushing its head. Frightened, I reached back into Ellen.

My son had died in her womb. There seemed to be a howl turning in every corner of the room.

I was only dimly aware of my hawk—his head, body, wings disintegrating, himself drawn instantly into spirit. I wrapped Ellen's body in my shadowy self; she was dying.

Some of the old tales about ghosts have a grain of truth to them. Not everyone makes it; some need help. Neither Ellen nor my son was strong enough to manage the transition without help. But I only had energy enough to bring one of them across. Ellen's life was real, ongoing; the baby's life was an imagined thing.

I had to choose; it was going to end for either Ellen or my long-awaited son. Only one would have a second chance, as a phantom.

I reached out for what remained of Ellen.

The hawk's spirit was too swift even for me to follow, a roaring through the room that took my son on into ghost before I could reach Ellen. The hawk made the choice for me. Ellen spilled out onto the floor like an emptied bag.

Ghosts travel widely. And all time is the same for us. I can see dawn rising out beyond the James River, and my hawk and son circling the Carillon Tower in their play. I cannot reach them; they soar too swiftly for me. But I still follow. My son pursues the onrushing hawkspirit as it heads out to sea, and I follow. It's a game to him, a race, and he giggles among the clouds. I try not to envy him. Our appendages seem winglike to us in our current form, dissolving in the dim light, becoming yellow, white, then transparent. Our imagined hawk claws trail into tendrils of silver rain cloud. My son dissolves so quickly out over the ocean, expanding into the morning at an ever-widening angle, so quickly I find him hard to pursue. But I manage to dissolve almost as quickly, mix into his thoughts my lost memories of bone and muscle. We enter the James one after the other and seem to set it afire; red and orange trails glow on the surface awhile before fading. In every flash of water, there's a fish. I can almost touch them. In every space of sky, a fish. Hanging there, luminous.

With large, pained eyes. Mouths howling love.

Gemini

BY
TANITH LEE

THE BELL.

By the oval window a bell rings.

"Nine seven," I say, because it keeps me a unit still, and not a person. Who knows? This might be a wrong number.

Beyond the window, the glass city stretches away.

"Hallo?" asks a voice. "Is that you, Geminna?" it asks me.

And the turquoise hills, and the blue hills.

"Yes. This is Geminna," I say, and inside me, *It* stirs.

"Why, Geminna, we haven't seen you for so long. We're going to the sea, Geminna. Come with us."

And the pale blue hills, like hyacinths.

"I can't," I say. "I'm sorry."

And the palest blue hills, like sky.

"Oh, but, oh, Geminna—I know there's your reading and your studies—can't you study with us at the beach, by the sea? Can't you, Geminna?"

"Another time," I say, "it would be wonderful."

"Oh." Rebuffed, the voice of a forgotten friend hangs adrift in the wires. I don't have many of these calls now. Soon they will stop forever. "If you're sure, then. Some other time."

And the pale silver sea.

But I can't go out.

It won't let me.

THE HOUSE.

This is an old house, stone and brick and stucco, a long ramble of a house, with many rooms and inner courts, and a long, wild garden with a high wall. Here I may do what I want. As long as I am alone. In the garden are mulberry trees and twisted hawthorn, and tall pines, and old stone urns from which spill beautiful rank weeds. Halfway, a river runs, several feet across, where fish glitter. A stone bridge crosses the river, and on the other side the wilderness rises in terraces to a faded white summerhouse. Beyond the summerhouse is the tower. This is the highest point, and from the tower-roof, ringed by the crumbling parapet, I can see all the city, the hills, even the sea, restless in the distance. Above, the stars turn and burn. In winter everything is white, and the sea opaque with ice floes.

THE SEA.

Sometimes *It* will let me go to the sea, for a little while. Then I walk barefoot in the cool water and the sand, smelling the old fish smell that the sea carries with it. I bring back shells and stones, and pictures I have drawn, or clicked with the eye of my little camera. Once a big dog found me, and we played by the sea's edge, in the salty froth. We ran backwards and forwards, laughing, until a man came.

I thought I would stay and speak to the man. He was young and handsome and the dog loved him, but *It* wouldn't let me. So I went away.

Dawn is the best time for the sea, or early in the morning, before the moon sets. There are not many people then.

THE HOUSE.

There is a lot to do in the house. It cleans itself twice in every ten days, and I help it. I like to cook from the deliveries that are brought to the service door. There's no problem there, of course. The door takes in what I need and pays the men, who then go away. They mutter and look up at the windows, blind with sunlight. Does anyone really live here? Books come, too. I have already a vast library: poetry, drama, novels, works of science and philosophy and magic. I don't always understand, but I try. My mind is opening little by little, like a rusty flower. I can play five instruments: the ancient pianos of the house, the harp, all the range of guitars which hang from mahogany pegs in the music room, the reed flute whose sound is uneasy, green, and my own voice which I have trained now to an extensive range. I also paint and sculpt, embroider, study the stars—I have much to do.

Often, very late or early, I walk through the city.

I have seen drunks lying in the road, or lovers in the parks. In winter the parks are empty except for the swans.

But people still remember me.

If only people would leave me alone.

BEFORE.

When I was a child, before *It* came, I knew many people, and children, but I was always more adult than child, and had no understanding with my own kind. They were like wild animals to me, but without the beauty of wild animals. They had to grow before understanding came between us, and then it was too late.

I was a born child, but my mother soon tired of me.

I don't remember her, only my guardians, who were kind and did not stay long. And, of course, I remember the name she chose for me. She called me Geminna, after the golden twins of the Zodiac, but she didn't know how apt that name would be.

At sixteen I received this house, an ancestral possession, and my citizen's pension, enough to keep me. I have all I need, and more.

SERVICE.

But there is no complete escape.

Every three months come the ten days of Service, my duty to the city.

It is my spring fear, my summer terror, my autumn horror, my winter despair.

This is where I meet these people who linger and cling.

I seem to fascinate them because I am remote.

They want me because I am always moving away.

THE BELL.

The bell rings.

"Nine seven."

"Ah, yes. Am I speaking to Sol.Geminna Mavern?"

"Yes."

"Sol.Mavern, I am to inform you that your three-monthly period of service is due."

"Thank you."

"We have on record your request for isolated labour. This time we suggest you report to the Library of Inanimate Beauty. This is more or less a solitary post, where your studies may be continued and also used to profit the establishment."

"Thank you."

"You will commence Service the morning of the day after tomorrow. The twenty-fifth of the month. Your stated working time will be ten in the morning until sixteen hours. Your instructor will meet you in the outer hall."

I have often wanted to visit the Library of Inanimate Beauty, but I couldn't. And now—fear.

Darkness.

THE DAY IS HERE.

The day is here.

I rise, bathe, and dress in inconspicuous pale black, a dress reaching almost to my ankles, and a wig to hide my hair. The wig is a dull but pleasant brown. My own hair, the golden hair of the golden Twins, attracts too much attention.

Hypnotised by the pale green of the breakfast grapefruit, I can hardly eat it. I drink wine with my coffee, and then more wine without coffee. And then . . .

And now I must go.

I leave the house.

The succession of old doors clang to behind me, shutting me out. Will I be able to return?

There is never this panic when I leave for my lonely walks. This panic is only because I am going where *It* does not like me to go.

The streets surge with people.

Their teeth glint like eyes; their eyes, like teeth, bite my peeled face. A river rushing nowhere sweeps me along. The crowded public cars, the dust, and morning slapping the city across the face. I look back. On the hill, an old mansion. Mine.

There are cascading trees in Palmer Street which leads to the Library of Inanimate Beauty. I think I have come this way before.

White steps, tall slender Martian pillars, each wound round with a bronze snake.

The doors, having recognised me from my Service card, slip open and close behind me.

Now.

Now *It* begins. How can I explain what happens, this intangible terror, the great waves of thick silence beating at my head.

But my instructor is coming.

"Good morning," we say to each other.

He guides me, gliding through the roaring chasms of fear he does not see.

"Sitting room . . . garden . . . food is brought in . . . these books . . ."

He is telling me all manner of things I shall have to discover for myself, later.

He is a big man, like an overfed dog, but plain. Because of this, *It* does not torture me too much. Any sense of quickening at a new presence, and *It* would ring me from end to end with agonised jealousy.

Half an hour has passed.

We drink thin delicate tea, and now he is going.

He is gone.

A SORT OF PEACE.

It washes back into *It*self but I can feel *It*, waiting, watchful. *It* will never let me be completely at ease in this new place. There is no guarantee that others may not come, even though I have been told I shall be alone.

But compared to what I was before, now I am liberated. I take off the hot wig and *It* pangs in me:

'*Be careful.*'

I wander from room to priceless room, among the ice-limbs of statues, the turning harps, playing, the mosaics and paintings, glass and books. Today people will not come in until fourteen in the afternoon, and by then I will be in my own apartment with my work. Tomorrow the Library will be shut, and mine all day. After that it will be open all the time, and I shall hide, quite safely, but out of reach of this beauty.

There is a golden sun, inside the sun a crystal, inside the crystal a lion of some black glossy material. It sings at the touch of a switch.

The apartment where I am to work is cool and lofty, lined with books, and looks out onto a small walled garden. My instructor has left me a list of instructions, despite our meeting.

I catalogue the books and the music tapes, reading some and listening to some. It is leisurely and enjoyable work. I have been very lucky this time. On the great plaster sheet, four feet by six, I plan the painting they have suggested I might try for them. It will be a panel in one of the walls of the Library, something rich for the whiteness of the room.

Of course, I will make it the Twins.

Slight, muscular, white-bodied beauty in yellow robes, their long hair like marigolds. They are so alike that it is only their sexes, male and female, which makes the slight difference between them, but her breasts are very small, and he has no beard. Around them are paler yellow leaves and darker ocher leaves, copper flowers, and the enormous limbs of old trees. Geminna and Geminni, in their mind forest, hand in hand, a golden incest of the soul.

My meal break comes, an optional hour—shorter or longer if I wish. I sit in the garden, hot with sun, eating a peach. I am almost, almost at peace. It is still. Quietness.

A VOICE.

A bell rings.

I look up, and see it ringing in a niche in the garden wall. I stare at it. It rings and rings. It occurs to me that I must answer.

I answer.

"L.I.A. three five."

"May I speak to Sol.Mavern? I believe she's working there."

"Yes, this is Sol.Mavern."

"Geminna!" The voice tells me a name, and says she met me three months before, when I worked in the Gallery of Light. "May I come to see you? Now, perhaps."

"I have a lot of work to do," I say.

"Oh, now, Geminna. You know no one expects you to work *hard* at anything. You always were so conscientious. I shall be there at fifteen, after the Library opens."

THE TRAP.

I put on the brown wig and wait, in my trap, as the sun slants down the sky. At fourteen the doors open, and people wander in. Distantly I hear the extra activity as things whirr and sing, shapes dance, and colors musically change. I put away the books and continue with the Geminni, but my hands are trembling.

She comes early.

Her dress is a scarlet that hurts my eyes, her movements, fluttery and agitated as a bird's, hurt my eyes. *It* hates her. She flickers into a chair. I summon tea for her and slices of orange, and she smokes long silver cigarettes which make her an aura of silver perfumed smoke.

"Ah, yes . . . so long . . . the party, a simple thing—you never came. . . . You promised us you would. This place . . . old . . . boring for you. . . . Dinner . . . you must come then. Oh, you *must*. So many men, dying to meet you. It *is* a *man* that you'd be interested in? I have other friends. . . . Such a recluse! Geminna, you are so *elusive!*"

I say, I think, the correct things. I hope she will go soon. She does not. She is suggesting that we walk to a cafe or wine-house at sixteen to celebrate our reunion.

"I'm afraid I can't," I say. "It's impossible."

"Oh, it always is!"

She laughs. *I* am impossible.

At last sixteen comes and we leave together. My apartment locks itself behind me. She walks beside me in the open street, where every shaft of sunshine is too brilliant, brittle like glass, (we may crack the light by moving through it too quickly) and her voice is splintering the air.

At a corner she leaves me, amused sourly at my rejection. I am white and drained. But I am going home. I seem to run the last yards. My doors fly open, shut fast behind me.

The vise *It* has held me in all day relaxes.

I.

I am looking at my face.

It is looking at my face.

Small, pale, tapering, all color drawn out of it into the gold hair. Sometimes plain, sometimes ugly, sometimes beautiful. A changing face, a face like a year, with seasons, days and nights. When I am beautiful, *It* feeds on me, staring out of my own eyes into my own eyes. I have sat half an hour before a mirror, hypnotised, till *It* had had enough.

This is the morning of my fifth day of Service.

Tomorrow and the day after are my rest period, and I may stay at home if I want. After that, another five days and then freedom. Until the next time. It has not been so terrible after all. The girl in scarlet rang me again, but she didn't come to see me.

THE INTRUDER.

I walk through the streets, half shut against the noise and movement, and come to the Library of Inanimate Beauty.

Inside I find my instructor. A brief shock. *It* grasps me hard as if I had betrayed *It* and must be punished—as though this unexpected intruder were my fault.

"You look surprised, Sol.Mavern," I hear him saying. "Don't be alarmed. Your work is excellent, I must say. The mural-panel is—"he spreads his hands—"I wish we could attach you to our staff permanently."

In the book-lined room, he summons tea which we drink. He is talking and talking. I wonder why he waits. Suddenly he takes my hand. The touch is electric but horrifying. Alien contact. As if he had burnt me, I snatch away, and *It* writhes in me like a serpent.

He laughs, uneasily.

"A quiet dinner," he says, part of a sentence I have missed.

"No," I say.

I think he has seen *It* in my eyes, hating him. Now it is his turn to recoil. He clears his throat, gets up.

"Someone else will be joining you this afternoon, Sol.Mavern. I hope you'll be kind enough to show them the work that must be done."

Icebergs are splintering and clashing in my head as he goes.

Always I have hated to be touched, because *It* has hated it, furious at my violation. Now I cannot be calm. *It* will not let me be. Once a man, long ago in one of the periods of Service . . . he pulled me to him. He was a handsome man, and *It* detested him more than most. The dark room was red with blood colour as he forced my mouth towards the chasm of his mouth, and *It* was a cobra smashing my spine. If I cannot get away, *It* will kill me, kill me rather than let another being have me, even for an instant. I am not very tall or particularly strong, but I thrust the man away from me. *Its* strength worked through me.

Now *It* would like to kill the instructor, and cannot, and so *It* hurts me instead.

When calm comes back, I recall what he has said.

Another one is coming.

Another outsider, another alien.

And I must—

THE YOUNG MAN.

I am painting now, and while the colour and the pattern absorb me, I can almost ignore *Its* iron grip, tightening, as we wait.

I look into the face of Geminni. He looks at me. His face is beautiful and cruel. He holds Geminna tightly by the hand, his other hand stealing towards her breast; claiming her and holding her tight.

The brown wig is very hot. I can't take it off.

Outside, the hum as people move between the statues and the music.

Another sound.

The door of my apartment slides open.

I can't turn. I stare into the face of Geminni, who lashes me with thorns across the old scars of other lashings.

"Can I come in?"

Almost the voice of Geminni, young, male, a beautiful voice.

"Of course."

I must look round now.

I look round.

Damn them, damn them. They have sent me a handsome man.

No, a beautiful man. Young, sapling, lion's hair, eyes like blue knife blades.

It leaps. Like a sea-dragon *It* leaps.

I see him staring at me, this young beautiful man. He looks—delightedly amazed.

"I'm sorry," he says, "I expected an old hag. A woman working alone among books and objets d'art—I'm not sure how I formed such a ridiculous impression. And you're not."

He flushes slightly, giving so much away at once to my silence. His skin is clear, pale, the tough, gold, male hair along his jaw a surprise after the smooth hard softness, almost metallic, across his cheek bones.

I consult the name on his Service card.

Sol.Cyprian.

I can't see the name, but I have memorized the name previously.

"Sol.Cyprian?" I ask him.

He grins.

"Oh yes. Very formal. Try David."

It is eating me alive as I tell him I am called Geminna. He looks from me to the panel, but I whisk him towards the books and music tapes. I have learned my lines for two hours. Now I am word perfect. I see him staring at me as I explain the work he must do. He is puzzled by me. Friendly and attractive, he is used to any response but this. He looks curious, quizzical. When I finish, he wanders back towards the

Geminni, wanting to talk to me about it. But I go away. I close myself in the rest room, and sit on the long couch, and the beating sea retreats, leaving me cast up like a dried-out shell on the beach of despair.

Far off, unreal, I hear a flight of planes pass overhead.

LATER.

Later, it comes to me I must go back. I walk into the room, every sure step the creeping of a terrified insect. I cannot seem to focus as I balance before my painting. I am aware that he sits reading, looks up at me from time to time, still curious. He does no work at all. Ignore me, grow bored with me. You are so beautiful I cannot be quiet. The whole room is full of your presence as if of the sound of the sea, or of some incense burning. I am burning. My hands, my lungs, my eyes are scorched out.

What is the time? Tension has stretched minutes into a thin bright sharpened stake to pierce me. Only fourteen. I cannot bear two more hours of sharp crystal. Where is escape? There must be escape. Sea waves churn and turn and roar through the hollows of my body, until I am blind, deaf, numb, defeated, caring for nothing except release. I do not even question *Its* cruelty any longer. I accept all, all, only find me some way to obey you, and so be free.

"Tell me," he says. I hear him from a great distance. It occurs to me that he is not real, a nightmare only. "Do you disapprove of me as much as you seem to? I mean, if you like, I can really do some work."

"Please do what you want," I say.

He smiles, gets up, takes his book into the little walled garden. The sun shines on him. Golden. He is no longer in the room. The transparent doors close softly, dividing us. I will go now. Nothing matters. Excuses can be made later—I am ill, perhaps, or have forgotten some vital personal errand. . . . I slip out of the room, make a way through the people in the Library. The streets are full. Sunlight bursts on the white glass towers of the city, the million windows. There is so much *light.*

THE HOUSE.

Evening purples the oval windows of the house into stained glass. Cool garden darkness hangs over the river. I watch the fish and think of nothing. There is a great calm in me, like the sweet cool peace which follows the cessation of great physical pain. Deliberately, I do not think back over the afternoon, or forward, ahead of the next two days which are mine, for both these avenues of thought are sharpened to hurt me. My image evolves like a ghost on the dark water, disturbed a little by the fish. This is how it is with me, to stand forever, disturbed a little, wavering, distorted, forming again, but always transparent. But there is a reason. There must be a reason. Am I special? Yes, yes, *It* whispers in me. Unique, singled out from the rest—the ones who run in herds. Am I? For what purpose then? The purpose is myself. Why then? There must be some answer, hidden—where? And what?

DREAMING.

I am dreaming. I know I am dreaming, because when I am asleep, *It* is no longer with me. Asleep, I am often with people, and it does not seem strange or impossible then, neither am I afraid. David Cyprian is waiting for me in Wilton Square, before the marble portico of the airport. I see very clearly the blue and white flagstones laid out in patterns under our feet. He takes my hand. His touch is familiar yet wonderful. My hand is delighted at its contact with his hand, which is so much larger, dry and cool as a leaf. We walk under the portico. My hair is the colour of his, though lighter. I see our reflection in the long mirrors of the walls and, though we are different, we are similar, like brother and sister. Music tinkles through the airport, as I have heard it sometimes, awake, standing outside in the star-frosted dark. A page of the dream turns. Now we are in a little plane, lifting straight into the blue air above the city, rising and rising. He turns and kisses me on the mouth and his mouth is like the world all brought together and given to me in one moment.

I open my eyes and am awake. *It* grips me at once, strongly, fills me and bursts me open. Betrayed, vengeful, *It* rips every memory of pleasure from me, and leaves me empty in the silence.

THE HOUSE.

Two days pass very swiftly. I have done many things, played much music late into the night, finished the embroidered hanging that I shall put up on this wall which faces the garden. Dusk brings uneasiness. I wander across the lawns, the river, the terraces, around the summerhouse. I climb the steps of the old tower. The city stretches to the hills, a net of neon stars spread over it.

Tomorrow.

I will not think about tomorrow.

MORNING.

It is morning. I rise, linger over bathing, linger over breakfast without eating. Now is the time to leave. I do not leave. I walk from room to room. An ivory clock-face shows itself, threatening eleven o'clock. I will not think.

Now it is almost twelve. It is impossible that I should see him again.

The very *thought* of seeing him again—is impossible. I go to the wall and touch the bell. I ask for the Committee. I explain. I am ill, but very willing to complete my period of Service when I am well once again—in ten days, perhaps? They agree, are sympathetic. I will have to sign a form, of course, which they will send me. But I must not distress myself. They will arrange for my duties to be resumed once I am completely recovered, and everything is perfectly all right. Relief is wonderful. Breathtaking. It was so easy, I am suddenly ashamed. I will not think of this. I am safe. This is all that matters. And whoever else will be there in ten days' time, it will not be him. He will be gone, his Service over. It was so easy.

Will he wonder where I am? Will he wonder why I am not there? Will he remember me at all?

I.

The day of unexpected freedom is full of an exciting refinding. I read a great deal, and it seems to me my progress is accelerating. In the sunset I dress in the long white dress with its winding embroidery of yellow flowers which are the same shade as my hair. We stand before the mirror. I touch my own hand in the glass, and seem to feel the contact of flesh. We are one. I am whole. *It* lights up my heart like a warm flame. What does anything else matter?

THE DOOR.

There is a sound. I recognise the sound as the noise which the door makes when someone comes to it to be admitted. The noise is rare yet full of menace. I sit frozen among the white roses, the candles, the wine glass frozen into my hand. Seconds skitter away. The noise comes again. The core of me holds itself tightly. Go away, whoever you are, go away. I wait. The noise comes. I rise, look about me. Will they stare in at the windows? Will they see the lower rooms where I have sat and walked and lived? Will they climb the walls by some incredible means, stare through into this room and see me imprisoned here in the vivid candlelight, a fly in amber? The door sounds again. So persistent. Who is it that is so persistent? Anyone else would have gone away, thinking me out. I wait.

The door is silent. I count the seconds, then the minutes, standing still at the centre of the room. Slowly the core of me relaxes. My hands unfreeze from the glass which breaks in pieces on the floor. They have gone.

It comes to me suddenly that I must check the lower doors of the house—particularly the glass doors to the garden. I cannot remember that I have locked them—these doors which in this old house must still be bolted and barred. And yet, how seldom it is that I forget. . . . I take a candlebranch, afraid of the harsh revealing ceiling lights. I go down the stairs, across the hall, into the room where the candles touch gold on the embroidered hanging. I go to the glass doors, and beyond them, in the dusk garden, I see a man's figure.

THE VISITOR.

He has climbed the garden wall after all, its delapidation providing dangerous but successful footholds. He is dusting himself down after his jump from the top into the patch of purple weeds at the side of the house. He looks up and meets my eyes, and comes to the doors. He opens them before I can move, and is in the room with me.

"I really am sorry," he says. "God knows what you must think. You don't even remember who I am, do you? David Cyprian—we met three days ago—look, when you didn't come back, I thought something might be wrong. Then this girl arrived—she said she was a friend of yours. She mentioned where you lived, and it's an out-of-the-way sort of place, isn't it? I dropped by after work—just on a sudden impulse— to see if you needed anything—you're on your own, aren't you? Then you didn't answer the bell. I thought, well, I thought you might be ill. Hence the rescue act over the wall." Suddenly he stops explaining. He takes in my appearance. "But I can see you're quite all right," he says. His eyes narrow slightly. "My apologies. I'll be going then. Can I use your front door, or would you rather I went back the way I came?"

I shut and lock the doors behind him. My hands are trembling; the situation is so strange I don't know what to do with it. I walk out of the room and he follows me.

In the hallway I hear him stop behind me. I too stop, as if at a signal.

"Tell me," he says, and his voice has changed again, "you *are* all right, are you?"

He is young and he is concerned. Unafraid of his own kind, he has an interest in them, an affection for them; he does not even understand that I am *not* of his kind. I turn to him, and become all pain and terror as *It* lashes *Its* serpent coils into my heart and brain. I stand and look up at him out of the vortex of my individual and special agony.

THE WORD.

"No," I hear myself say.

One word. One word of betrayal for which *It* will never forgive me. There is nothing more *It* can do to me than *It* will do to me now, for now *It* will kill me. And yet. I am looking into his face still, seeing in his face the lost world drifting away, out of my reach forever, which is foolish, for how can one lose that which one has never possessed? And then I am angry. Anger comes like a biting howling thing; never before have I experienced this madness which exults in its own extremities.

I run towards the stairs, up them, and he runs after me.

"Wait!"

I run into the music room. The candles smoke. He stands at the open door. I run to the pianos and my fingers sparkle over the decaying keys like scurrying diamond rats in the erratic light. I pull the guitars from their pegs and break their hearts open in brief insanities of song. I run out, and he lets me past. I run into the library. I pull the books in showers of white and scarlet from the shelves. Science and philosophy, poetry and magic lie like severed flower heads at my feet. I turn and look at him, and I see he is startled, afraid almost of what I have become. It gladdens me. Now *I* am fear also. And the fear in me, the never-slackening vice, becomes his fear, not mine, so that I glory in it. I run out, down the stairs across the house. My fingers fumble at the locks of the glass doors, and then I am running in the silent darkness of the garden. Pines, the tortured hawthorns, over the stone bridge, the river below me. The summerhouse—a white clock-face deprived of hands—timeless, is forever. The terraces, the tower. And then comes stillness, for there is nowhere else to run.

Below, the city. Beyond, the hills fading into the sea. Stars blink at the brightness of the city's stars beneath.

BY THE PARAPET.

I stand by the parapet, listening. He is gone. No. I hear him come out on to the tower roof behind me. He is afraid of me. Why has he followed me?

He comes to stand beside me. Why is he here? He is at a loss. I can't grasp his sense of obligation. If only he would leave me alone. In that moment he reaches towards me. A second later I understand that he only meant to touch my arm, guide me back from the edge of the tower roof. But in the moment when I feel the pressure of his hand, I am certain that he will kiss me, and his mouth will become the world. And *It* leaps in me. Like a sea-dragon *It* leaps. Always I have hated to be touched, because *It* has hated it. Once, a man, long ago . . . If I cannot get away, *It* will kill me, kill me rather than let another being have me, even for an instant. I am not tall or particularly strong, but I thrust him away from me. *It* thrusts him away from me.

And, losing his balance, the crumbling parapet is all that can support him. And the parapet does not. In an incredible little burst of snow-white breath, the old stuccowork falls apart like the mummy dust in the violated tomb.

DEATH.

I accept because I must.

I accept my difference. Understanding follows acceptance. Understanding of the defences I must not allow to be breached. Nothing else matters. Preservation is the foremost instinct. Ultimately, we kill to survive. Even so, the responsibility is not mine, could never be mine. *It* knew the threat against *It*self. *It* acted. The blade, the bullet, the bomb are not assassins, it is the hand which uses them. I also have been put to use. *It* did what *It* must.

When I think of death, it does not offend me. Death can be beautiful. There need be no stigma of any kind attached to it. Grass and rank flowers, the powder of old stone, the silence, hold all the elements of the wreath, the grave, the monument, the requiem.

The garden reclaims all things into itself.

I put the books back, and the guitars on their pegs. I have begun a new embroidery, larger than the last. Soon I shall have to complete my period of Service, but not yet. There is a lot to do. I shall have no time to go to the tower for many weeks, but the stars are very patient and enduring.

The house is full of peace.

THE BELL.

By the oval window a bell rings.

"Nine seven," I say, because it keeps me a unit still, and not a person. Who knows? This might be a wrong number.

Beyond the window the glass city stretches away.

"Sol.Mavern?" asks a voice.

And the turquoise hills and the blue hills.

"Yes," I say, and inside me, *It* stirs.

"Sol.Mavern, I'm speaking on behalf of the Committee. We're making inquiries about a young man—a David Cyprian. I understand you worked a Service period with him quite recently?"

And the pale blue hills, like hyacinths.

"It's possible," I say, "but I don't remember. I'm sorry."

And the palest blue hills, like sky.

"I see. In fact, it was your last Service period—I think you left some days early because you were unwell?"

"Yes. Perhaps that's why I don't remember. There was a young man, I believe. I can't recall his name."

"Then you wouldn't have seen him at all since the third of the month?"

"Oh, no," I say. "I didn't really know him."

"I see, Sol.Mavern. Well, I'm sorry to have troubled you."

And the pale silver sea.

But I can't go out.

It won't let me.

Perhaps *It* will never let me again.